HOW THE PYRAMIDS WERE BUILT

Peter Hodges

HOW THE PYRAMIDS WERE BUILT

Edited by Julian Keable

ELEMENT BOOKS

© Julian Keable 1989

First published in Great Britain in 1989
by Element Books Ltd
Longmead, Shaftesbury, Dorset

Printed in Great Britain·by
Dotesios Printers Ltd,
Trowbridge, Wiltshire

This book was designed by Lisa Irving, Sarah Moysey and Andrew Williams,
students of the Department of Typography & Graphic Communication,
University of Reading.

It was designed on an Apple® Macintosh™ using
PageMaker® 3.0 software and output on a
Linotronic™ 300 imagesetter.

The book is set in a PostScript® version of Palatino®,
manufactured by Adobe Systems Incorporated.

British Library Cataloguing in Publication Data
Hodges, Peter, *d 1980*
  How the pyramids were built
  1. Egyptian pyramids. Construction, ancient period
  I. Title II. Keable, Julian
  690'.68
  ISBN 1–85230–127–9

Contents

List of tables and maps

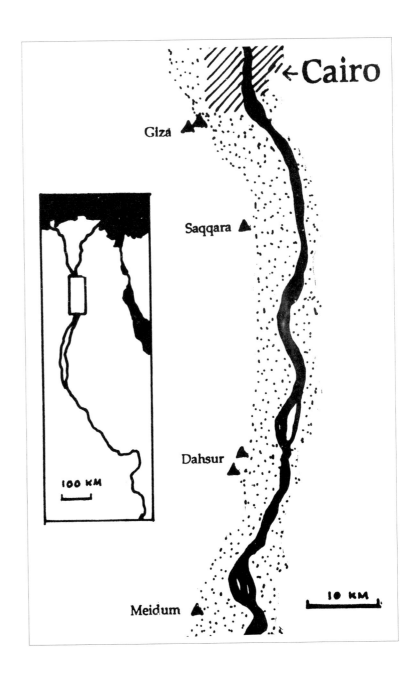

Map showing the location of the six principal pyramids referred to in the text.

Foreword

The background

It is for us a lucky chance that Peter Hodges fell ill of the famous "pharaohs' revenge", shortly after arriving at the Mena House Hotel: that is to say, within sight of the Great Pyramid. He had been profoundly struck, as anyone must be on first confronting this monument, by the immensity of the building task. But whilst immobilised in the hotel, his mind was hard at work. Having accepted, as we all have, the 'ramp' theory, without examining it, there at the spot he found it lacking in not one, but several fundamental respects. He lay there, and within three days had arrived at the essential germ of the idea developed in this book. It is an immensely bold idea, immensely simple – and to his way of thinking, the only possible way to achieve the result. That is why he insisted on his title: *How the Pyramids were Built*.

Peter was far from being an arrogant man. He was, however, proud of being a builder, and always referred to himself as such. He felt strongly that building should remain a 'trade' (rather than be designated a 'profession', a modern trend favoured by many Associations), but he was himself unusual in having had a professional training as a builder, at the School of Building, Brixton, at a time when the great majority of builders were brought up in the trade and passed directly into family businesses. Peter was educated at King's College School, Wimbledon. His family background united quality craftsmanship with an enquiring intellectual ability – cabinet makers, fine furniture restorers, an uncle who wrote a standard work on hydraulics. After being retained at Brixton to finish his course, Peter served with the Royal Engineers as a sapper officer in the field during the Second World War. Subsequently, he worked with a variety of building firms before taking over a long established and respected business. By the time he became interested in the pyramids of Egypt, he was a builder of wide experience and knowledge, who knew a very great deal about the practical problems of building, and about how to solve them. He knew what could go wrong, and that if things can go wrong, they generally do. He knew at first hand how to work stone, and felt a direct affinity for the men who worked the stones at Giza. He knew just how difficult it is to raise four angled corners so that they reach a point in the sky – at the first attempt. He recognised that the pyramid builders were engaged in the top technology of the time. Subdued and fearful gangs of slaves have no place in such a scene – but a respect for repetitive manual work certainly has, a respect which is born out of the evident orderliness of the building operation, as well as its scale.

Peter's wartime experiences as a sapper were an important element in his approach to the question. There he learnt the power which leverage can exert, and the value of the skilled application of this power; the value too, of co-ordinated teamwork.

After that first concentrated effort, which led to his vision of the 'autostatic' building method, he worked as he could to research and develop his ideas. It was only then that he discovered the description by Herodotus which so closely echoes his theme. During the course of his work he realised the need, if only for his own peace of mind, to demonstrate practically one way to carry out his idea. Clearly, the exact details can be varied; the exact methodology can be developed – but this is unimportant besides the principle itself of building directly from the ground.

Peter wrote his book for ordinary people, not for experts. He was not an archaeologist, nor an historian – it was the practical building problem which interested him, and which he thought would interest others. However, his fresh approach will stimulate all who are interested in the unsolved mysteries of the past, expert and non-expert alike. That is why this book is being published now. Sadly, he died in October 1980 before this could be achieved, though the manuscript itself was in full draft form. My own involvement only began after his death. Although my wife and I had met Peter and his wife Margaret occasionally, over many years, and had come to respect both of them for their integrity and quiet, careful thoughtfulness, we had no idea of Peter's work on this book. How we regret that now!

However, after Margaret had hesitantly offered to lend me the manuscript to ask my opinion of it and I had read it through at a single sitting, I found myself compelled to stay with it, to revisit Egypt, to help if possible to follow up indications given by Peter and to assist in the publishing process, so that his work should see the light of day.

The manuscript itself is largely as he wrote it: and includes most of his original illustrations. Peter knew that more work was needed on the text, and expected that the diagrams would be redrawn professionally for publication. Certain editorial notes and maps have been added, where these are germane to the text, and are clearly marked as such. Peter's original illustrations have been retained because they are sufficiently clear and their directness is characteristic of the man. Peter's diagrams showing the outline of St Paul's, London have been augmented by St Peter's, Rome, and the Apollo spacecraft.

Peter's widow, Margaret, has helped in interpreting minor ambiguities and supplied much background material including additional references. Without her dedication and attention to detail, this book could not have appeared.

The text

In studying the text, and in discussing it with knowledgeable people, three things became clear:

1 That the huge problems involved in the 'ramp' theories had not been explained fully enough. Peter saw them so clearly, that they were to him self-evident, once mentioned. I could see that this was far from the case, so I have attempted to develop this argument in a separate article. It now appears to me that problems associated with 'block-flow' dominate all others – a single ramp (or even four!), especially if operated for a mere three months in each year, is out of the question, since blocks must arrive at the working plane at the rate of two every minute, throughout a twenty year period!

2 Peter proposed that the 'accretion' theory was wrong, and that the largest pyramids were built level by level. Whether or not they continued to arrange internal 'steps', as at Meidum, but constructed as the pyramid rose, or whether they abandoned the stepped approach, is of no real importance to the main 'autostatic' argument. It would seem at least possible that this very conservative Ancient Egyptian culture did continue with the (to us) unnecessary inner steps. Since there is evidence that the (later) pyramid of Menkaure (Mycerinus) was built this way, it seems quite likely true of Khufu and Khafre too. But, I have heard no one dispute that the work must have been done layer by layer; this is the main point.

3 Peter proposed a particular, and special, form of lever, having its own heel at the fulcrum. It occurred to me that a straight lever would avoid a number of difficulties: (i) no special design, shod in metal, is needed, (ii) the length between toe and fulcrum can be varied at will and (iii) the tool would be even less easily recognised for what it was than that of a specially shaped lever, if found today. I have therefore added the results of my own work on this line, and added to his practical experiment the further step of lifting a notional 'core block' up a notional 'pyramid course'.

Since his death, at least some of the confirmatory evidence he hoped for would appear to have been forthcoming: the facing stone chippings at Giza, (reported by Michael and Angela Jones, *JSSEA* (1982), 1980 Season, in their study of the Temple of Isis) and the 'setting-out' marks, including permanent water channels at each corner, (reported on by Mark Lehner, *JARCE* vol. XX, 1983). Moreover, doubts about the ramp theory itself have surfaced, as expressed by Martin Isler in *JARCE* vol. XXII 1985, *On Pyramid Building*. He proposes a method with some points of similarity to Peter Hodges', but shrinks from Peter's bold refusal to see anything but the pyramid itself as the scaffold.

More to the point, the negative evidence that ramp material has not been found leads to the question – if not built as here described, then how?

Julian Keable, 1989

Chapters 1–10 and Appendix

by Peter Hodges

1 A new look at the pyramids

The greatest of the pyramids in Egypt, those at Giza, are not only vast and spectacular monuments built to a unique shape but are also buildings having a structural property which sets them apart from almost everything else that man has built in brick or stone. They were constructed without the use of any enclosing scaffolding or any form of temporary access which did not itself become part of the finished structure. When the last stone had been placed the craftsmen needed only to carry away their tools from the site before leaving the pyramids standing complete and accurate in their true geometrical form.

This statement may be quite contrary to the generally accepted picture showing great gangs of workmen dragging stones up specially built ramps in order to reach the rising structure, but this book sets out to show that the greatest of the pyramids are of such a size and construction that they could only have been raised by men standing and working on the structures themselves. The chapters will trace in practical terms, the evolution which began with the erection of simple stone walls, progressed through the building of stepped pyramids and reached a climax in the construction of the largest of the Giza pyramids. There will be no attempt to encroach upon the archaeologist's art of establishing the motives or religious needs which caused these monuments to be raised; this book offers a description of a building method sufficient to enable any intelligent person (given time and the skilled labour) to supervise the building of another Great Pyramid by the same uncomplicated methods employed by the Ancient Egyptians.

The reason why we can show today how the Egyptians must have raised their pyramids is simply that the disciplines of the task allowed them no choice in the method of building. Given the same resources, there was then, and is now, only one way to build a pyramid. The truth of this very definite statement will emerge as subsequent chapters examine the details of masonry practice and also the evidence which is offered by the shape of the stones and their placing within the structures. We could usefully classify into one genus those structures which were raised by men who stood only upon the structure itself and used no scaffolding. In the absence of a common term to describe this particular method of working I would offer the word 'autostatic' to define any structure raised in this manner. An autostatic structure is unlikely to have vertical sides but would be of a shape that reduces as the height increases, such as a pyramid or a cone. The use of a scaffold would have been unnecessary, if not impossible.

In England, in the county of Wiltshire, there is an autostatic mound called Silbury Hill which is over 300 feet high in the shape of a truncated cone with smooth grass sides (see fig. 1). This can only have been formed by a 'building' operation and qualifies as our English 'freehand' pyramid, built by men experienced in the construction of steep-sided ditches and ramparts. Elsewhere in the world the classification includes the Egyptian pyramids and the Mexican temples. In Ancient Egypt the method came as the final step in a progression which had begun with the use of hand-sized stones to construct walls, continued with the raising of stepped pyramids using larger stones and led to an era when stones of huge weight could be used to build vast pyramid shapes which still stand today, despite time, weather and the vandalism of later generations.

Fig. 1 *Silbury Hill, Wiltshire, England.*

These monuments possess a further special property in that they can be increased in size without changing their basic shape. Every pyramid, however big or small, possesses the same majestic qualities, but the finished size is a direct reflection of the resources available from within the community. In theory, at least, a pyramid could be built or enlarged to almost any dimensions, but in practice there must be a limit to the amount of time and material which could be made available after meeting the prior demands of the community to live and defend itself. A building with vertical sides could not be extended upwards indefinitely because it would either topple over or burst out at the sides, according to the type of material being used. Furthermore, such a building could not be built from 'upon itself' but would need a temporary scaffold to be erected which, in ancient times, would have limited the height and the size of stones. A pyramid was the only shape which the Egyptians could have used if they were to raise such high structures.

These early builders understood how stone could resist a great deal of pressure but if it were used in the form of a beam to span

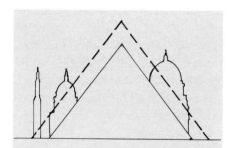

Fig. 2 *The Great Pyramid, 481ft high, drawn with St Paul's Cathedral, London, 364ft, St Peter's, Rome, 456ft, and the Saturn launcher with Apollo, 363ft, all drawn to the same scale. The outer dotted line indicates how little would be the increase in height if the volume were doubled.*

an opening, then it would readily break. In more recent times we have identified that a beam develops compressive stresses along its top surface and tensile stresses along the bottom and we can design structures with suitably resistant materials in the right places. Reinforced concrete is an example, with the concrete resisting the compression and the steel the tension. Having learnt how stresses develop we can design great frameworks of wood or metal but the Ancient Egyptians had to rely on a material which gave resistance only to compressive stresses.

There is evidence that pyramids have been enlarged after the builders had reached their first target, but figure 2 shows how little a pyramid would grow in proportion to the volume of the material added around the outside. If the base sides were extended by only one tenth in length, the operation would require nearly a third more in volume of material.

Many writers have put forward theories as to how the pyramids might have been built, but these theories have usually dealt with only a small part of the whole building process; some theories that may appear comprehensive fail on examination to satisfy necessary practical requirements, as I shall show.

The idea that pyramids were in any way difficult to build would never have arisen if the structures in Egypt had not been so vast that they generate an atmosphere of incredibility. In trying to investigate the methods used we find it hard to come to terms with the practical problems involved and even to imagine how the stones were lifted into place, let alone set down to such accurate dimensions. The buildings are there as proof that the work was done and, as we know that the Egyptians at that time had only manpower at their disposal, then we, with our modern knowledge and greater experience, should be able to deduce how it was accomplished.

I had thought, at the beginning of my research, that the most difficult part of building a pyramid was the raising of the great stones so far above the ground, but I came to discover that it must have required much greater skill to set them down again, neatly jointed so as to reproduce the true pyramid form on such a large scale.

The Ancient Egyptians were able to come to terms with the huge numbers and the enormous size of the stones used in the greatest pyramids because they had worked their way up from much smaller beginnings. The Great Pyramid was raised towards the end of a continuous evolution and if we study this, step by step, we shall come to understand the competence of its builders. The same skills are still in use today, but we take them for granted and do not immediately recognise the connection.

Scientific man has made his progress by discovering and exploiting a continuing series of new energy sources. The Ancient Egyptians made their progress by developing their skills on the natural materials of wood, stone and water, with the result that they advanced much further in their mastery of these basic substances then we can readily appreciate today. In our age we have become accustomed to discarding a technique before it is fully exploited in order to explore another innovation. Understanding and appreciating the Egyptian's competence requires us to revert in our minds to a time when there were no other energies or materials to be anticipated, and when the stone lying in the strata below the ground was the only material which could be exploited to provide enduring buildings or monuments. Every urge to progress was channelled naturally into making larger and better structures from the different types of stone that lay to hand within the Kingdom.

Since the Ancient Egyptians did not record their building methods, it may seem as though the pyramids were built in an age of mystery, divided from us by a dark band of time in which all knowledge and skill was lost. In reality there is an unbroken line of personal skill stretching through the last fifty centuries, and it is this line which helps us to speculate intelligently as to the way in which the mind of the pyramid builder would have been working 4,500 years ago. As a student I learned to turn a rough boulder of stone into a true polished cube, and when recently I needed to confirm my recollection of the details I called on the local stonemason and talked to him about his craft. An Ancient Egyptian watching our conversation would have felt that nothing much had changed; he would have seen around him the same profusion of stone blocks and piles of choking dust and the same shaped tools being guided by the unchanged skills of hand and eye.

There is a popular idea that pyramid building continued throughout the thirty centuries of Ancient Egyptian history, but large all-stone pyramids were built for less than 200 years, a period no longer than the age of steam in Europe. The first signs of the Egyptians' urge to raise a tall monument came at Saqqara where Zoser built,* and later enlarged, the Step Pyramid about 2700BC, and the evolution continued rapidly until about 2500BC, when the Great Pyramid was raised at Giza, followed by Khafre's (the 'Second Pyramid'). During this period six large stone pyramids were completed, the last five of these during the sequence of three generations – grandfather, father and son. Subsequent to the building of the 'Third Pyramid' of Giza by their successor Menkaure, pyramid building declined in quality as well as size, so that the structures were no longer durable, and their remains do not excite curiosity outside learned circles (see table 1).

Placing the pyramids within a time scale which we can readily understand is not difficult, but to try and place them in a scale of weight or size emphasises how unlike they are to anything we have around us. The Great Pyramid stands in height between St Paul's Cathedral and the Post Office Tower, London, and yet in solid weight it probably exceeds all the buildings within the

*Ed: Peter Hodges always referred to the pyramids as having been built by the kings, or pharaohs; as an architect I feel it should be mentioned here that the first recorded architect, Imhotep, is credited with designing the various monuments 'built by Zoser', including the 'Step Pyramid' at Saqqara.

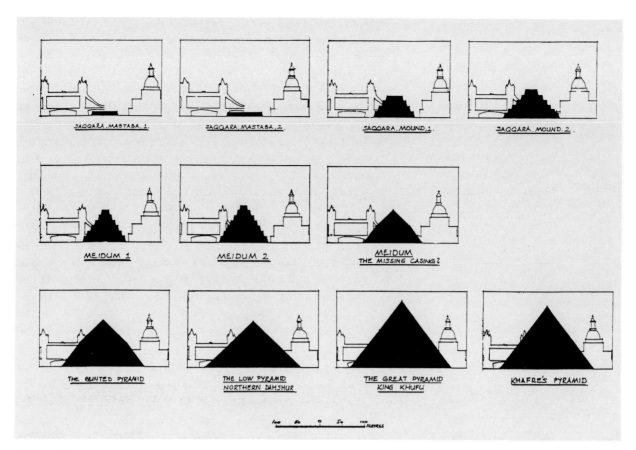

Table 1*

*Ed: the casing diagram for Meidum is conjectural and is discussed in chapter 6.

square mile of the City of London put together. A man can lift and handle a weight of about 80lb; the largest pyramid of all needed the equivalent of 200 million man-loads, a total of about 6,500,000 tons, all raised by human energy. We cannot grasp such a scale of weight because in our modern age we deal more in space than in mass. We use the minimum amount of material to achieve the maximum amount of volume in a finished structure. Our largest buildings are hollow but the pyramids are virtually solid, and their bulk is almost beyond our comprehension.

A detailed description of all the pyramids erected during the main period could occupy an entire volume and add nothing to what has been recorded in many other books, (*The Pyramids* by A. Fakhry is excellent,[1]) but it may be helpful to describe the size and general layout of the largest pyramid before discussing and analysing the practical methods of construction.

The 'Great Pyramid' was built as a tomb for Khufu and stands the highest amongst a close group of three on a stone cliff at Giza, seven miles from Cairo and overlooking the wide valley of the Nile, in such a position that the river would have reached the edge of the cliff during its annual inundation. The site is surrounded by the remains of some smaller pyramids and also scores of flat-topped tombs constructed to receive the bodies of the Royal Family, noblemen and senior officers of the royal court. In modern

Fig. 3 *The average stone in the Great Pyramid is cut in chunky proportions and stands about waist high. The courses are always level but are of differing thicknesses, although each individual course maintains the same thickness throughout.*

times* the horizon of the bare desert has been broken by a smattering of shanties set down by the inhabitants of Cairo to serve as summer retreats from the heat of the valley.

The pyramid base was originally constructed 756 feet square† covering 13 acres and with four sides which rose at an angle of 52° to reach an apex 481 feet high. The solid centre, or core, was formed of approximately 2,300,000 coarse limestone blocks, each weighing some two-and-a-half tons and each roughly the size of a modern kitchen sink unit (see fig. 3).‡ The outer faces were covered in a finely dressed limestone of better quality, leaving a true and smooth pyramid shape which had been as accurately formed as any modern measuring system could have achieved. Within the solid structure a series of passages and tomb chambers were formed during construction which required the use of stones weighing up to 50 tons each,[2] set on a precise, fine joint and dressed internally to leave smooth plane surfaces. These passages were finally sealed by the outer casing stones so that no visible trace remained to break the even outer surface of the sloping pyramid sides.

*Ed: there are three pitches which were used during the era of pyramid building: approximately 75°, 52°, and 43°. These could be called the 'battered face', the 'steep pitch', and the 'low pitch'.

†Ed: A. Fakhry states that "the reasons for the choice of angle are probably structural", and refers to J-P.Lauer's discussion on this.[4]

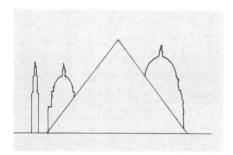

Fig. 4 *Normal view of a pyramid shown in text books, so that only the side slopes at a pitch of 52° are seen. The Saturn and Apollo space craft, and St Paul's, London are also shown.*

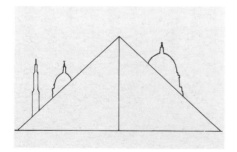

Fig. 5 *The same pyramid viewed from opposite the hip, showing the structure at its greatest width and emphasising the long raking silhouette at about 42°.*

Although the pyramid shape is normally associated with Ancient Egypt, it is still used today when it is necessary to construct a sloping roof over a square tower. This work is done by carpenters and I propose to use in this book the simple terms which they use to describe the surfaces and angles of the shape: the gradient of the sloping sides thus becomes the 'pitch', the meeting line between two adjoining sides the 'hip', and the summit the 'apex'. Historians and archaeologists have speculated a great deal concerning the angle of the pitch.* Some people have sought significance in the figure of about 52° of the steep pitch, the angle most often used.[3] However, if the pyramids are regarded from various points at ground level and from different distances, it is not the pitch of the sides which attracts the eye, but the long raking angles of the hips. These stand out against the skyline and lead in a noble gradient to meet at the apex. These hip lines, more than the sides, are really the essence of the shape and yet the angle which they form with the horizontal has hardly, if at all, been discussed or examined in writings on Egypt. The drawings show this comparison (see figs 4 and 5). It may never be known whether the Egyptians chose the shape of their pyramids according to the pitch of the sides or the pitch of the hip lines, but it is most likely that their choice was largely determined by practical necessity.† The three earliest of the principal completed 'pyramids' are not true pyramids at all and there is no evidence that they were ever intended to be so. The true pyramid form appeared only about halfway through the evolution (see table 1). Some theorists have studied the shapes of the completed structures and then tried modern formulae or mathematical standards against the ancient shapes. This process can only uncover a series of coincidences, of which none has yet been shown to have a direct root in the thinking or practices of the Ancient Egyptians.

In order to understand how the pyramids were built it is necessary to know not only how the Egyptians thought but, particularly, how they worked. The following chapters concentrate on the practical implications of their knowledge. Any speculations about their reasons for choosing a particular angle for the sides soon become overshadowed by the realisation that the finished shape was the best method of reaching the greatest possible height, using the least amount of material. The sequence of building during the pyramid era is an example of how the craftsmen's building skills will always control the scope of the designer and, perhaps, eventually decide the form or shape which is the most satisfying to the beholder.

The fact that we have such detailed knowledge today of a civilisation that existed 5,000 years ago is due to the skill and efforts of eminent historians and archaeologists during the last two centuries. Men of learning have searched through the hot desert sand to uncover the buildings and artefacts of the Ancient

Egyptians and then used the evidence to build up a picture of everyday life and religion, full of wonder to us in the twentieth century. The revelations of such an ordered way of life holds a marvellous fascination and can be likened to our walking in the darkness past a lighted window and catching a glimpse of the life within, alive with warmth, and touched with mystery because of its silence.

An archaeologist has the talent of re-creating history from evidence left by another civilisation but his background is one of scholarship rather than craftsmanship. It is not reasonable to expect an archaeologist to be an experienced manual worker in all the basic trades of living, from farming, building, husbandry, etc., through to embalming. A stonemason would immediately be at home amongst the sites of Egypt and could work the stone and construct the buildings as though it were a normal daily task rather than an intellectual exercise. We send an archaeologist to search for history but for practical problems we really need an investigator who could, if need be, carry through the solutions himself on the basis of his practical experience. This book examines pyramid building from this standpoint in some detail.

One distinguished Egyptologist, after spending many years among the earlier tombs at Saqqara has written "The stones could easily have been lifted by two men so that there was no need for mechanical assistance at that period".* I found that these stones measured 4ft x 2ft x 1ft and must weigh about half a ton each;† in practical terms, a twelve-man lift. Any sapper who has helped build a Bailey bridge will remember, only too well, that it took six trained men using carrying handles to lift and manoeuvre each bridge panel which weighed half this amount. These Saqqara stones were taken up some 200 feet above ground level. This contradiction in such a basic fact as the weight of the stones caused me to doubt if detailed problems of masonry practice could be properly identified and evaluated purely on a basis of scholarly experience, and the more I read in the way of theoretical comments on the pyramid masonry, the more I became convinced that the subject needed looking at from a new viewpoint.

The six principal pyramids given in my table 1 still display, in signs which are clear to read, a steadily progressing advance in the stonemasons' competence. It was a progression in which they never looked back; each monument is 'better' than its predecessor in one essential way that sets the pyramid era apart from other architectural developments such as the Greek, Roman or Gothic styles. Those later builders developed their skills to contrive ever finer, more graceful and delicate effects whereas the Ancient Egyptians, apart from improving the neatness of their work, devoted their whole efforts towards mastering larger stones which would constitute progressively larger solid shapes. Just as an architect can tell the date of a Gothic window by its style, form

*Ed: Peter Hodges left no specific reference for this statement but see reference [5].

†Ed: the stones referred to are from Zoser's pyramid, see chapter 6.

and decoration, so an archeologist could judge the place which any particular stone must have had in the Egyptian progression by assessing its size and character.

In the chapters which follow I have examined first the present theories together with a few old chestnuts. I have then dealt with the most dramatic problem, which is the raising of the great stones into place, followed by the details of a stonemason's method of working and finally with the building and casing of the pyramids.

In my readings through numerous books about pyramids and Egyptology I have come across, time and time again, the same photographs and drawings used by different writers. I am a builder and not an archaeologist and must view things from the standpoint of my own trade and my own experience; as a result nearly all the drawings and photographs in this book are original and will, hopefully, provide a fresh aspect of an old subject. The book is intended as a pyramid builder's handbook as well as a firm base for archaeological thinking.

Two different kinds of pyramid construction are identified and examined in this book, and these I call 'buttress'.and 'coursed' respectively. The former is my preferred term for what are commonly called 'step' or 'stepped' pyramids, because it arises essentially through a description of the construction method.

I propose to refer to the Ancient Egyptian kings by their Egyptian names, giving the version of these accepted at the time of writing (see table 2).

Table 2

It would be inconsistent to employ the Greek equivalents only for those few notable pyramid builders whose names are most commonly known. The following are the kings whose names appear frequently in this book:

Greek form	Egyptian	Dynasty
—	Zoser	Third
—	Sekhemkhet	Third
—	Khaba	Third
—	Sneferu	Fourth
Cheops	Khufu	Fourth
Chephren	Khafre	Fourth
Mycerinus	Menkaure	Fourth

2 Previous building theories

I propose to examine some of the theories which have been put forward by recognised authorities as being the methods which might have been used by the Ancient Egyptians in the building of the pyramids. The greatest problem seems to have been understanding the physical task of raising heavy stones up to the enormous heights at which we now find them. The essence of the problem is that a man needed to be given a mechanical advantage. For example, assuming that a man can lift and carry 80lb, then the face stones at Zoser's Pyramid needed 14 men each, Meidum 42, and at Khufu's 112 (see table 3, p. 54). These figures will help to put the problem into a perspective which everyone should be able to grasp. This point will be expanded in the next chapter.

A ramp is a device which bestows a mechanical advantage, but for raising large stones up to great heights it is inefficient, dangerous, and tedious in operation. However, Egyptologists seem for some time to have been almost obsessed with the idea that ramps were used for all the pyramids. I. E. S. Edwards, in his important book *The Pyramids of Egypt*, when dealing with their construction, quotes Herodotus' description of the building method reported to him, and then states: "In the absence of the pulley – a device which does not seem to have been known in Egypt before Roman times – only one method of raising heavy weights was open to the Ancient Egyptians, namely by means of ramps composed of brick and earth which sloped upwards from the level of the ground to whatever height was desired".[1] Many other writers could be quoted,[2] so the ramp does warrant an objective study: firstly as to the different ways in which one can be used; secondly, its possible shape or gradient and lastly, its construction.

A ramp can be used either as a 'short' or as a 'long' ramp. The 'short' is one where only the load passes up the incline so that the hauliers can either stand or walk on a level area at the top of the slope.

This is the most efficient method, whereas the 'long' ramp requires the whole train to work up the slope together thereby wasting much energy in raising the weight of the hauliers themselves, a considerable factor as their combined weight will probably be more than that of the load itself (see figs 6 and 7). A short ramp may be invaluable in a permanent situation such as an incline out of a quarry, but for building a pyramid shape its use is restricted to the lower levels because the working platform eventually becomes too small to accommodate the hauliers. No

Fig. 6 *Short ramp. Suitable for short lifts. The hauliers work along the level ground above the top of the ramp.*

Fig. 7 *Long ramp. The hauliers have to lift their own weight up the slope as well as the load they are pulling.*

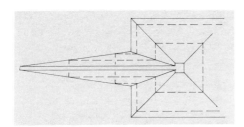

Fig. 8 *The plan of a ramp drawn by J-P. Lauer and repeated in many books. The dotted lines indicate that the ramp started short and wide, growing narrower and taller as the pyramid grew higher.*

Fig. 9 *I have turned the plan into an elevation, showing that the gradient of the ramp would be 1 in 3.*

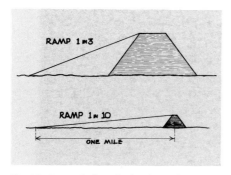

Fig. 10 *A ramp built to fit the plan in fig. 8 would look like the upper of these drawings, but the text establishes that any ramp would need to be no steeper than the lower drawing.*

building theory is worth study unless it encompasses the placing of all of the stones required and in particular those at the very top.

The long ramp is the one most usually depicted in books on Egyptology, when the drawing shows a pyramid, three-quarters built and serviced by a ramp with a gradient of about 1 in 3 (see figs 8 and 9).[3] This layout cannot be based on reason because it is a hard task just to walk up such a gradient and it would be impossible for hauliers to manage their work under these circumstances. However, it might be possible for a gradient of 1 in 10 to be used if the friction under the load could be reduced without impairing the foot-hold for the hauliers (see fig. 10). No one would use this method for raising stones today so we cannot study the device in use; the nearest I can get to reality is to walk up a slope which exists near my home. The gradient is 1 in 10 and extends for 100 yards (whereas a ramp to the top of the Great Pyramid would run for 1,600 yards), but it is a steady pull and quite enough to confirm my views that the largest pyramids would never have been built if this were the only method available.

The only paintings so far found on this subject that have been left by the Ancient Egyptians show loads being dragged on the level,[4] nowhere is work on an incline depicted. Anyone who has pushed a car along the road will have recognised that the effort is enormously exaggerated at the slightest incline. It is very difficult to put the problem of raising stones into practical context because we no longer use our own strength and skill to move heavy weights, we no longer have the 'feel' of the problem. It might be a comparison if we asked four men to carry a heavy coffin, without putting it down, from the door of the British Museum up a steady 1 in 10 ramp until they reached the Cross on St Paul's Cathedral (see fig. 11), a mile away, and 480 feet higher.

How could the Ancient Egyptians of the Fourth Dynasty have constructed these ramps? A mixture of rock and sand, if tipped

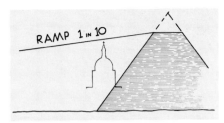

Fig. 11 *Side view of the ramp or causeway when the working platform is nearing the top of the Great Pyramid. The drawing shows that at this stage the ramp would be higher than the cross on St Paul's, London.*

Fig. 12 *Timber 'cribbing' being used to retain a loose fill of rock and earth during emergency repairs to a mountainside road which had been demolished by explosives.*

down would have settled with sides laying at the natural angle of repose, about 25°, so that the pyramid with sides pitched at 52° would have been completely immersed by the time the apex had been reached. This would have effectively prevented the masons from checking the shape of the structure they were building and also the volume of material required would have been astronomical. This problem could have been minimised in one of two ways: by adding mud to the mixture and revetting the sides of the ramp with stakes and wattles (as Silbury Hill, 30°),[5] or by tipping loose broken rock and binding the face with timber cribbing (see fig. 12). Even if sufficient baulk timber could have been found for such a mammoth task, the sides could hardly have been retained at a steeper pitch than about 45°. The idea of using any kind of loose material on this scale is unrealistic.

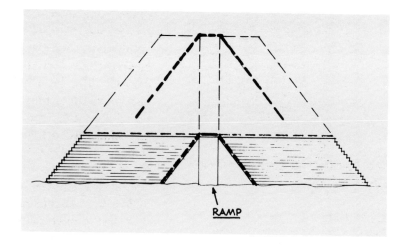

Fig. 13 *This diagram shows how one type of building ramp would appear when viewed from the end. It has often been said that as each course was laid on the pyramid the ramp was raised by the same amount and the battered sides of the ramp widened, as shown by the dotted lines. However, taken to its logical conclusion, the completed ramp would be as wide as the pyramid itself, and the problem of adding the stones to the sides of the ramp would be more difficult than building the actual pyramid.*

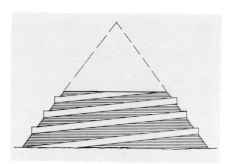

Fig. 14 *The spiral ramp. Several authorities claim that the stones were dragged up ramps built of mud bricks rising round the sides of the pyramid. This diagram shows how these mud ramps would have had to rest across the steps of the core. Although this solution is frequently quoted, in practice the difficulties would be insurmountable – it would be impossible to drag the heavy stones round the sharp corners; the ramps would obscure the shape; and would crumble under constant use over at least 15 years.*

The ramp therefore needed to have a stability equal to that of the pyramid, and in my opinion such a ramp would have needed to have been built of squared stone. At its greatest height the ramp's volume would have been three times as great as that of the pyramid itself. This volume could have been reduced if the sides had been raised at the same angle as the earlier buttress pyramids (75°) but the masons at that time had never raised this kind of face for a height greater than about thirty feet without adding a further buttress and indeed such an operation would have been impossible (see fig. 13). Once buttresses are added the overall gradient of the buttressed outline remains about 52° so there was no saving to be made in this direction. The only method available to the masons was the forming of a bonded structure with the courses inclined at 1 in 10 to the horizontal, a task which would have taken them three times as long as the building of the pyramid itself and would have left a vast residue of stone.

It might be thought that these problems with the volume of material would not have arisen if the system of attached or peripheral ramps, suggested by Dows Dunham and frequently mentioned,[6] had been used. This theory holds that ramps of mud-brick were formed around the four sides of the pyramid as it grew and that gangs of men dragged the stones up on sledges (see fig. 14). The gradient of the ramps would have had to be increased, or the number reduced as the pyramid rose because the distances between the ramps would lessen at each turn.

The term 'mud-brick' is another way of saying that the ramps were made of dried earth, a material quite unsuitable to withstand the constant traffic, year after year, of heavy loads and thrusting feet. The ramps would surely have crumbled away or fractured downwards on a plane of shear. One artist has shown wooden sleepers laid across the earthen surface,[7] but these would soon have worked loose under the disturbing pressures, as also would have stone pavings. My sectional drawing discloses the relationship which would have existed between two successive

Fig. 15 *Section through spiral ramps.*

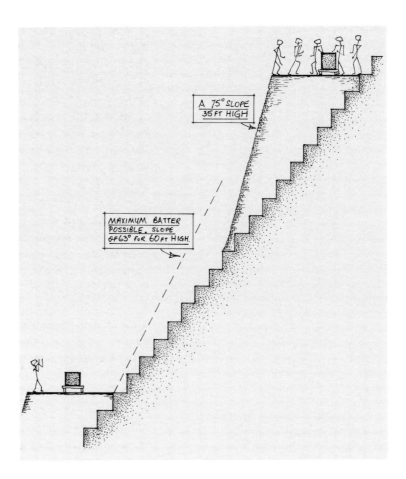

ramps (see fig. 15); no civil engineer could accept the stability of such construction even with the ramps thickened by splaying out the face as far as possible – a move which would have cloaked the pyramid face entirely. The builders would have had great difficulty in starting a firm foundation for the ramps, with the base line running upwards diagonally across the steps.

Finally, there would have been one operating fault serious enough to have stopped the process long before the apex had been reached: because of the length of the train, the stone would have come to a halt a long way short of a corner. The men could neither have walked out into space nor found room enough for all of them to have got two hands on the stone and pushed it round the corner. The theory of these attached or peripheral ramps is really not tenable.

To summarise the usefulness of ramps: it is clear that the 'short' could not have been used when approaching the apex of a true pyramid, and that the 'long' would have posed impossible building problems and only provided a device of little practical use.

It has been stated that "evidence would appear to demand, that ramps were employed by the builders of the Pyramids...".[8] M. Zakaria Goneim, Chief Inspector of Antiquities, Saqqara, states categorically (also, like Edwards, after quoting Herodotus):

*Ed: i.e. Giza

"the only way in which the huge blocks used in the later pyramids* could have been hauled into position was by means of ramps built against the side of the structure".[9] This statement cannot rely on evidence because there is no such evidence at the coursed pyramids at Giza. The evidence which has been recorded appears to relate only to much later and quite different structures, in which case it should be ignored, or to the earlier buttress pyramids of the Third and Fourth Dynasties. Those pyramids are smaller and are of a different construction; the extent to which ramps could have been used in such cases, and probably were, is discussed later in chapter 6, on the basis of evidence that has come to light at Saqqara.[10]

There is a drawing by L. Borchardt which shows ground marks pointing towards the Meidum buttress pyramid,[11] and he has claimed that they show the base of a construction ramp. A further drawing,[12] possibly also by Borchardt, has been reproduced which shows the entire ramp but the proportions of this are so impracticable that the speculation really establishes the reverse of the theory, namely that the shape of the marks proves that they could never have been the base of a construction ramp. Such a ramp would have needed a base width of about 400 feet if it were to reach the summit but we are shown a structure which, in order to fit on the ground marks, is so thin that it could never have been stable. The proposition is quite beyond the style and capabilities of contemporary masonry and, at a gradient of 1 in 3, would have been impossible to use on such a scale.

If we restrict our study concerning ramps to the buttress pyramids then some acceptable deductions can be made as to how the stones might have been handled. I put forward my own theory for a method by which a 'short' mud ramp, or a series of them could best have been used at Saqqara and Meidum, based on two items of evidence. Firstly that the stones are generally of a long rectangular shape in contrast to the 'chunky' stones in the later pyramids, and secondly that rope-making was a contemporaneous skill.[13] My drawing shows how a stone may be rolled up a steep slope with the aid of at least two long ropes, depending on the length of the stone (see fig. 16). The mechanical advantage, (a factor of six), does not become dissipated in friction, the ramp surface is not broken up, only a few men are required to hoist and

Fig. 16 *Using a short ramp.*

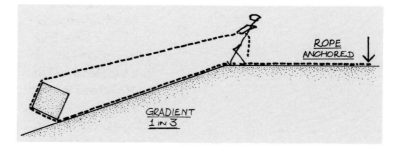

*Ed: Peter Hodges had intended to enlarge these arguments; see my additional material on ramps (pp. 111–24).

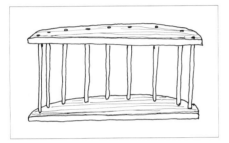

Fig. 17 *This 9in model of a wooden cradle was discovered in a foundation deposit at Deir el Bahri and it was claimed by Petrie that large versions were in general use during the building of the pyramids. (Similar models can be seen in the Cairo Museum). There is no way of judging how large the original cradles may have been. Their use is discussed in chapters 3 and 7.*

they can stand in one place while they haul in the ropes. The method is simple, quick and efficient – one which might well have occurred to men who must have been used to rolling stones over and over on the quarry floor, rather than picking them up. The community had an adequate supply of labour and material to provide the many long ropes needed. If this theory can be accepted then we can visualise short ramps being used against a stepped pyramid and also from the top of one buttress, sideways up to the next.[14] This arrangement has been shown in earlier drawings but without any practical understanding as to how such steep ramps could have been used.*

Amongst many previous theories on the general practice of pyramid building are those emanating from the 'rocking cradles' (see fig. 17) discovered in foundation deposits.[15] Those models have no scale, so we have no idea as to the size of the originals and the theories about their use have been purely conjectural. The cradles are suggested as being the means whereby stones were raised up the stepped sides of a true pyramid. I have copied a drawing by Sir William Flinders Petrie,[16] and then added my own to show that the stone would have over balanced while the next wedge was inserted, unless restraining ropes were put around the stone (see figs 18 and 19). The operation could not have been done on the pyramid step itself because there had to be room for the stone to lean inwards; the timber trestle would have been essential (see fig. 20). The system might have looked more hopeful if the stone had stood at right angles to the pyramid, but this is not what Petrie has shown; in fact no sort of re-arrangement will offer a successful use for the cradles in this manner. Several Egyptologists have tried to find a use for these 'cradles' but if they had looked first at the building process and detailed each sequence then a need for a tool of this shape would have come to light (see chapter 7).

Another theory is that of the 'double fulcrum' method (see figs 21 and 22), also depicted by Petrie for the same purpose.[17] A weakness must be suspected at once because he has chosen to show a long thin stone rather than the chunky core stone which makes up most of the core in this type of pyramid. I have drawn in the pyramid steps to add scale to his diagram and also indicated a few of the men who, it was claimed, operated the scheme by walking from end to end of the stone, creating a see-saw. Even if safety stops had been placed under each end of the stone, the scheme is quite impracticable because the enormous weight would have crushed the fulcrum or toppled the supporting packing.

A further theory suggested that a type of gallows was erected on each step of the pyramid, but with the cross-tree pivoted on top of the upright so as to swing round, rather like a crane with a horizontal jib.[18] The stone would have hung from one end while at the other several ropes were provided so that the men could

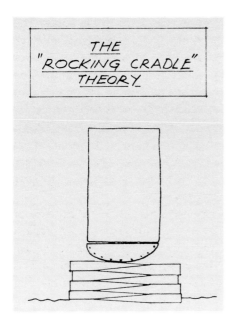

Fig. 18 *The 'rocking cradle' theory.*

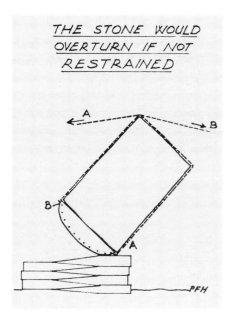

Fig. 19 *The stone would overturn if not restrained.*

Fig. 20 *Rocking cradles in operation: an unstable device.*

pull out and downwards to swing the stone up on to the next step. Assuming that the longest available cross-tree would have been about 24 feet and a lever advantage of 2:1, then the pulling arm was about 16 feet and needed some 25 men to pull together. The combined weight of the load and the men would have been about five tons, a dynamic load which had to be balanced on top of the pole: an arrangement which must have quickly developed a fatal instability. The greatest weakness in the theory must be the strength required in the cross-tree; a two-and-a-half ton load at eight feet from the fulcrum produces at rest a bending moment which can only be resisted by a piece of first quality timber (cedar

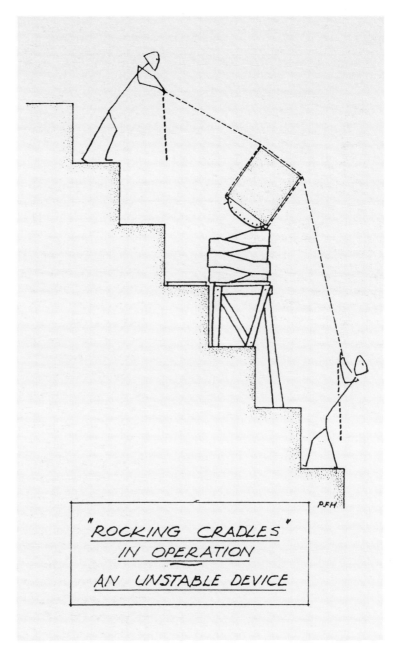

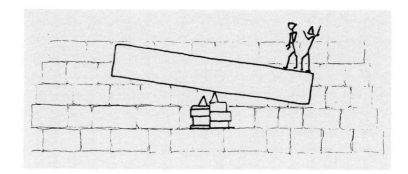

Fig. 21 *Double fulcrum theory.*

*Ed: cedar is known to have been imported into Egypt from pre-dynastic times (almost certainly from Syria, the famous 'cedars of Lebanon'):[19] but as a fast growing wood of the coniferous family, it is not generally regarded as suitable for load-bearing purposes.

would not have been suitable)* with a cross-section about 8 inches wide by 15 inches deep. The Egyptians had the competence to strengthen the timber with copper plates but even this would not have been enough to withstand the extra stresses set up by the load 'bobbing' up and down. Each gallows would have needed an elaborate structure requiring constant repair or renewal, and of course about 200 of these had to be in use together to achieve any useful rate of block flow. The theory finally defaults because no sort of gallows could ever have dealt with the largest stones which had to reach the roof level of the burial chambers.

I have examined these theories not merely to expose their impracticability but rather to show that any theory needs to be extended to its completion. In the area of pyramid construction this can best be done by observing some of the traditional skills and practices in use around us today.

Fig. 22 *Unsuitable for the average core block.*

3 Raising the stones at Giza

Herodotus, the Greek writer, visited the pyramids at Giza some 2,000 years after they were built. He listened to the Egyptian guides and amongst all the stories that he recorded was the following passage, a lucid description of how the stones of the Great Pyramid were raised into position:

> The method employed was to build it in steps, or, as some call them, tiers or terraces. When the base was complete, the blocks for the first tier above it were lifted from ground level by contrivances made of short timbers; on this first tier there was another, which raised the blocks a stage higher, then yet another, which raised them higher still. Each tier, or storey, had its set of levers, or it may be that they used the same one, which, being easy to carry, they shifted up from stage to stage as soon as its load was dropped into place. Both methods are mentioned, so I give them both here. The finishing-off of the pyramid was begun at the top and continued downwards, ending with the lowest parts nearest the ground.[1]

Now, almost 2,500 years after his visit, as we read these lines we should be able to recognise that such a method was the only one which could have been used to handle stones of such weight and in such numbers. This chapter establishes that the method explained to Herodotus was indeed the correct one and that the story had been handed down by word of mouth, without any exaggeration, through some eighty generations.

Perhaps because it was thought to be a myth, rather than a factual record, this description has been discounted by many, who regard the writings of Herodotus as merely legends, recorded by a gullible reporter. To some archaeologists the solution may have appeared too simple; they may have felt sure that such vast structures could only have been raised with the help of some extravagant system.*

It was after I had formed my own theory as to how the pyramids could have been built that my researches led me to read this passage by Herodotus, and I took his words as strong evidence of confirmation. I have explained in chapter 2 why sloping ramps would not have been suitable for the larger pyramids. The Egyptians must have evolved a simple method for raising these great stones, because no artificial source of energy was known at that time and no amount of religious fervour could alone have achieved such a gargantuan task. The method needed to be simple and at the same time safe, rapid, flexible in operation and, of course, powered only by man.

*Ed: translations of this important passage by Herodotus vary. It is possible that the use of the word 'machines', employed in some translations, rather than 'contrivances' as used above, has led to misunderstanding.[2, 3] My father, after reviewing the original Greek text, commented that whilst *machane* eventually became our 'machine', it originally implied a 'cunning device'.

The true nature of the problem does not seem to have been properly understood, yet its essence can readily be indentified. A stone is so dense that not enough men can get a 'purchase' under it to effect a direct vertical lift.

The men could handle the smaller stones used in the earlier Third Dynasty walls without much difficulty, each stone being lifted by two men or, if necessary, four men using a plank or cradle to hold the stone. It is interesting to note that the Third Dynasty stones at Saqqara, where these occur on the outer pyramid face, weigh about half a ton and were somewhat elongated in shape, making them slightly easier to handle. The squat stones at Giza needed a more sophisticated technique and it is this problem which I propose to examine in this chapter.

The use of a cradle with carrying handles can be discounted even for the average core stones used in the Great Pyramid at Giza because these would have needed teams of over 70 men. The method chosen had to be one which would also encompass the very largest stones and these were some 20 times heavier. The only substitute for a direct vertical lift is a contrivance that gives a mechanical advantage to a man's effort, and it is in these words 'mechanical advantage' that the solution must lie.

There are two distinct methods of raising any load; from above by 'hoisting' or from below by 'lifting'. This distinction is important because the Egyptians of the Fourth Dynasty, having no wheels, pulleys or cranes, instinctively tackled their heavy loads by lifting them upwards from beneath and, if we are to understand the thoughts of these men, we must try to reason as they did and view problems from within their own cage of experience.

The title of this chapter uses the phrase 'raising the stones', conjuring up a vision of the stones being taken up several hundreds of feet above ground level, but before this could be done they had to be lifted through that first vital few inches in order to get them off the ground. Even if part of their journey was made on sledges, in slings or up ramps, they still needed to be handled in detail several times; if we can come to terms with this more intimate movement, we can more easily understand the greater achievement.

I was fortunate to have approached the Giza pyramids on horseback, riding through the village at the edge of the plain, below the escarpment of the cliff, climbing up to the higher level at a point south of the main site, and then turning towards the pyramids across the desert. Such an approach avoided the motor vehicles and tourist parties of the twentieth century, so that my confrontation with the pyramids became a more personal one. I had read the guide books and the better-known authorities who had all described the great ramps used in the construction of the pyramids; but these pyramids appeared to be so vast and permanent alongside our human scale, and the height so enormous that I could not see any sort of temporary ramp being a part of their construction. But, if the guide books and the historians were wrong, there had to be a correct solution and in thinking about this I realised that I had often helped with the raising of loads heavier even than the largest stones in the pyramids, yet using nothing more sophisticated than men exploiting the principle of the lever. The job had always seemed to be a matter of routine and I had never stopped to consider whether the loads under my control were in any way abnormal.

It was the sight of the pyramids stripped of the facing stones to reveal the stepped sides which caused me to discard the old accepted theories of ramps, and suggested in their place a practical method that must have been the one used by the Ancient Egyptians all those thousands of years ago. I recalled to mind the image of small teams of sappers grouped at one end of a Bailey bridge and bending to work the jack handles in rhythm, raising or lowering the bridge during the final stages of its hurried construction. This mental image gave me the clue as to how the Egyptians might have looked, raising the stones steadily up the stepped sides of the pyramid.

My photograph (see fig. 23) shows one end of a bridge being jacked up in order to remove the rollers used during construction

Fig. 23 *Four sappers lifting one end of a 30 ton Bailey bridge using two simple lever jacks, each operated by two men. Heavier bridges, up to 60 tons, were raised as easily using four jacks.*

and to substitute the permanent bearing plates. The bridge shown was about 60 feet long, had a weight at launching in the region of 30 tons and could readily be handled by four sappers using two jacks. Longer and heavier bridges needed double this number but the jacking principle remained the same and involved no more than the conversion of movement into greater power. The jack shown has a solid square column toothed on one side and with a pad at the top and a toe at the bottom. This bridge is resting on the toe and each time the handle, which has a fulcrum in the casing of the jack, is pressed down, the column rises about one third of an inch and is automatically held up on a ratchet. The Ancient Egyptians seem not to have had ratchets but they could easily have inserted packing under the stone as the lever handles touched the ground, thus securing the maximum gain in lift before the levers were removed (see fig. 24).

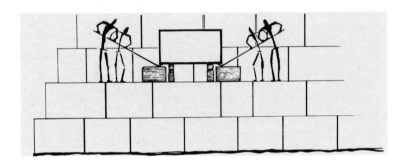

Fig. 24 *Teams of men could quickly raise the stones from step to step up the pyramid. Timber packing would be inserted after each 'jack' by boys working on the step below. The stones for the core weighed about two-and-a-half tons and the teams would soon have brought their work to a fine rhythm, raising a stone halfway up a pyramid in the space of a day.*

The use of manpower is by no means always inferior to mechanical power when heavy loads are to be moved. Experienced men working together as a team have a flexibility in the control of their power and an instant response to the needs of the moment. From the raw materials of nature men can prepare their own food, house themselves and pass from place to place over mountains and across water to group and re-form as the size of the task dictates. Modern machinery is superior in power but it does need special fuels, constant maintenance, and the larger and heavier it becomes then the more difficult it is to get it set up at the right place and time. Many a wonderful machine has spent days wedged up a mountainside or stuck firmly in the mud while the waiting men idled away valuable time. Both men and machines wear out under frequent use but at least the human race regenerates itself for further tasks ahead.

The idea of using a lever to increase the power of man's own energy has been with us since man first used tools as extensions to his own hands and arms. The lever does not produce energy itself, it merely allows us to concentrate our own movement and energy against some strong resistance and to move this resistance, although only a short distance. Almost every mechanical contrivance we use today involves the lever principle, including the simple bottle opener, the hand brake in a car and the toggle of an electric light switch. The Egyptian pyramid builders, having no energy source but their own, would have evolved a sophisticated control over the use of levers in order to exploit this energy, and as the basic principles involved have not changed during the intervening centuries the potentiality of the lever can be examined just as easily today.

The simplest example of the lever principle to be seen is that of two people at opposite ends of a see-saw, swinging up and down either side of a central fulcrum. If one person is greatly heavier than the other then he must move towards the fulcrum and, being closer, his weight will now have a lesser swinging effect. In simple arithmetical terms, a child weighing 6 stone, and 8 feet from the centre, can be balanced by an adult weighing 16 stone but only 3 feet from the centre. Both 6 x 8 and 16 x 3 equal 48. In this case the child is lifting an adult by placing himself nearly three times further away from the fulcrum.

The extreme example, used to concentrate power over a short distance of travel, is the pinch bar, better known to some as the 'jemmy'. The tool is used to generate enough power to split apart materials which are firmly fastened together, such as packing case lids, locked doors, tyres on a wheel rim, etc. There is no requirement to make a great deal of movement, as once the materials are parted the need for power has ended and the materials can be moved further by hand or other means.

The Egyptians, however, needed to develop a lever which could produce a usefully balanced mixture of power and movement, as the stones for the pyramids had to travel a considerable vertical distance. I have suggested the dimensions of such a lever in my Appendix, (photographed in use, figs 25–8), and it can be seen that the critical factor must be the strength of the material available for its construction. A longer toe will give greater vertical movement but this will call for a greater thrust on the end of the handle, thus increasing the stress across the heel to a point when this will bend or break. The only material available to the builders would have been a suitable wood, possibly strengthened or shod with copper.*

Petrie did discover and illustrate models of two bronze levers,[5] believed to date from the Nineteenth Dynasty (at the end of the pyramid era) but, apart from these models, I have seen no record of levers being found by archaeologists. However there is evidence of lifting points for levers in the form of bosses and slots on stones in pyramids of the Third and Fourth Dynasties, and Petrie states (my italics): "the practical shifting of blocks *in detail* was doubtless done by levers".[6] It must be remembered that objects in general use would have survived only if they had been too large to be destroyed or if they had been so small that their loss would not have been noticed at the time. The only exception to this generalisation would be those articles preserved in a tomb as part

*Ed: copper was worked from an early date and there are copper tools of excellent quality from the First Dynasty. Opinions differ on the use of any hardening techniques – Petrie states that copper tools of the Old and Middle Kingdoms were "generally hardened by arsenic". Lucas says that 'hammering' was "the only secret of hardening" known to the Ancient Egyptians but that arsenic and other impurities were always present "accidentally". The copper chisel referred to in chapter 4 contains approximately two-and-a-half per cent of arsenic.[4]

Figs 25 and 26 *One end of a two-and-a-half ton test load being lifted by two levers. A block of stone of the same weight would be smaller and more easily balanced on the stepped side of a pyramid, the men standing closer together, side by side.*

Fig. 27 *The point when the heel of the lever needs to slide forward under the load.*

Fig. 28 *A vertical gain has been secured by the insertion of extra packing.*

*Ed: the pharaohs needed a 'solar barque' too (see fig. 29).

Fig. 29 *The south face of the Great Pyramid. The modern structure in front encloses the timbers of the solar boat which was discovered below that spot quite recently; the boat was provided for the dead king's use during his life after death.*

of a burial, sometimes incarcerated in their original form and sometimes substituted by a model, to serve the needs of the afterlife. The design of the ancient tombs omitted any form of actual doorway for the spirits of the dead, either to the external air or even into adjoining rooms, as it was believed that they could pass through solid walls without hindrance.[7] Their needs for the afterlife comprised only food, the most immediate of daily personal belongings and, of course, for nobles and the Pharaoh, a staff of retainers.*

Any shelter the dead might have required had in any case been provided for by the structure of the tomb itself, and the layout of this had no doubt been supervised by the deceased during his days on Earth. There was no further need for the tools or materials of the building trade.

The levers in daily use would have been carefully kept until the handles broke or the toe became worn beyond repair, and at that stage both materials could have been used again: the wood as fuel for the fire ('kettle wedges' the workmen call them nowadays) or perhaps cut down to form some part of a smaller tool, while any precious metal would have been melted down for some other use. The levers would have been too valuable to be left lying about and too large to be casually dropped and covered by the debris of the building work.

The essential elements in the design of a lever can be better understood if the method of working is studied in some detail. The wood needed to be straight-grained and strong, and, whereas today ash is the most suitable English wood, the Egyptians may have had access to another tree with similar qualities – acacia is suggested by Petrie, and mentioned by A. Lucas.[8] It may have been possible to train certain branches into a shape natural to the knuckle of the lever and thus add greatly to the strength but, while this is pure conjecture, it can be assumed that pieces would have been selected from the tree so as to make the best use of the natural grain. Levers made entirely of metal would have been unnecessarily heavy and would have used a great deal of scarce material. As the lever was pressed down, the underside of the head would have slid forward, so that part could usefully have been shod with metal, and also greased with animal fat during use. The point of the toe would bear a concentrated load underneath the stones to be raised and would therefore also have benefitted from being shod or capped with metal.

The Ancient Egyptians did not of course design such a lever as an isolated project, as I have done. Starting from the use of a simple blunt piece of wood to help with the smallest stones, the tool would have been refined by succeeding generations, the demand created by the use of progressively larger stones being matched by an improvement in lever design.

The stones, when stored, would have been kept clear of the ground by a piece of packing to allow room for the insertion of the lever; there would have been plenty of odd chips of stone lying around the quarries or building site which could have served the purpose. A vertical lift would have been started by slipping four levers under the stone and then pressing down on the handles, producing a gain of, say, four inches before thicker packing was slipped under the stone and the levers removed. These could then be operated again, resting on their own platforms of packing and the whole cycle repeated until the stone had reached the level of the next step. Assuming a step three feet high, this would have needed about nine lifts, taking a practised team about a quarter of an hour. The sequence is shown in my drawing (see fig. 30).

When the new level had been reached it was necessary to 'inch' the stone across on to the next step by skilfully swinging the levers round horizontally while the weight of the stone was taken on the toe of the lever.

This part of the sequence has wider implications and needs to be examined in more detail, because it suggests that the levers could have been used to effect horizontal as well as vertical movement. The drawing shows a plan view of this operation and establishes that my 'standard' lever could produce a horizontal movement of nine inches (see fig. 31). This means that, provided the stone had to travel over reasonably level ground and the 'lifts' were made at a faster rate than those in the vertical work, the stone could have travelled through 45 feet in an hour. In long distance terms, this means that less than two days would have been needed to traverse the whole length of one side of the largest pyramid. This alternative method for moving stones horizontally rather than by dragging them on sledges over the ground, uses fewer hauliers, takes up less room and obviates the necessity of

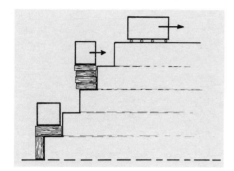

Fig. 30 *Diagram showing a side view of how the stones were jacked up and rested on timber packing pieces. When the stones reached the working platform, they could then be pushed or dragged on rollers to the part of the working platform where they were needed.*

Fig. 31 *Sideways travel. Diagrammatic plan showing how the standard lever could be used to move a load horizontally. The levers would need to be pressed down as they were swung across so that the lifting point 'A', under the stone, would describe as nearly as possible a vertical arc. A practised movement like this would be useful for moving heavy stones where there was insufficient room for sledges and dragging teams.*

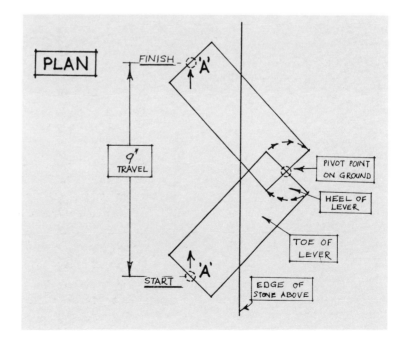

restricting movement to a prepared and levelled track. I believe that a stone during its passage from the quarry to the pyramid would have been handled by a mixture of the two methods.

Petrie discovered and illustrated certain fragments of flat stones dating from the Third Dynasty and bearing circular indentations,[9] doubtless made by a lever heel pivoting on the stone. This bears out my theory that levers were used also for moving loads horizontally, but it is a pity that the surface of these circular marks does not appear to have been analysed to detect whether it was metal or wood that had turned upon them. A study of the profile of the marks might give a clue as to the shape of the lever. Petrie's drawings show only a plan view of the circular marks.

The recorded studies in Egyptology are profuse in theories but very spare in practical experiments, despite the availability of cheap labour during the nineteenth and early twentieth centuries. All the necessary materials were to hand in Egypt yet there seems to have been little serious experiment into the handling of large stones or theories conceived from practical experiment. Every theory should be put into practice at a suitable scale and I have tried to do this with levers made to full size and operating on a full test load of two-and-a-half tons (the average weight of the Great Pyramid core stones). From these experiments I have learnt what it would have felt like for one of the Egyptian builders to take his share of the load when four of them lifted a core block. The operation feels deceptively easy and the blocks look deceptively small when seen by their thousands in the side of the pyramid, but in fact each stone possesses a lethal crushing strength and a potential for savage destruction should it get out of control.

Starting with the object of obtaining a four-inch lift and choosing six feet as the maximum convenient handle length, I designed and had made a series of wooden levers, as described and illustrated in my Appendix. The Egyptians had several hundred years of experience in the development of a lever, but I had to decide what was the most likely design that they could have achieved to give the best convenience and efficiency. I began with a strong looking thickness for the knuckle and tapered this down throughout its length to a minimum diameter of one-and-three-quarters of an inch, being the least that a man can properly grip in the palm of his hand when thrusting downwards. The angle between the toe and the handle is critical as this needs to be such that when the lever is pushed under the stone before the lift starts the handle is not too near the vertical. The haulier needs to get a good 'purchase' with the tool before he pulls it down with all his strength. The handle needs to lie flat on the ground as the stone reaches its maximum lift, and thus an experienced man can keep it down with his foot while he waits for the packing to be inserted. At this point the toe has come up to an almost vertical position and there is hardly any thrust to bring the handle back up again. The knuckle must not be too thick, otherwise the toe will not pass well under the stone and away from the fragile edge.

The Egyptians would have worked in teams made up from villages or families and I can imagine that there would have been keen competition in speed, coupled with safety. One stone allowed to tumble down the stepped side of the pyramid would have caused great havoc and loss of life below.

The chances of such a disaster were much less than would have been the case if stones had been dragged upwards along sloping ramps. With the lever system the stone was nearly always in a level and stable condition and was never more that a few inches above some form of temporary packing; consequently, if a stone slipped, it would come to rest before gaining dangerous momentum. If the hauliers became tired they could safely rest, probably leaning on the stone itself; but a stone being dragged up a slope would have been a potential bomb liable to crash down the ramp, at an increasingly lethal speed, if a rope parted or a man stumbled. It is not only the immediate effects of an accident which cost precious life and valuable time, but also the consequent effects which may well expand into a major disaster. With this in mind, any successful lifting system must operate to keep the loads under close control.

The practicability of the lever system is so fundamental to the system of building outlined in this book that it led me to make the experiments already referred to, and shown in photographs (see figs 25–8).

The diagram shows my calculations for lifting the average two-and-a-half ton core block in the Great Pyramid (see fig. 32), but it is also necessary to establish the possibility of handling the largest blocks which now lie inside the structure. It is difficult to be certain as to the weight of the largest stone used at this period because writers tend to vary in their recordings and some have perhaps quoted earlier surveyors rather than measure the stones for themselves. It is not unknown for such figures to grow with constant telling, but it would be reasonable to take a stone of 50 tons in weight as the largest which was used and to establish a

Fig. 32 *Diagram showing calculations for a simple lever to raise the standard core stones of the Great Pyramid. Four men, each with a lever, would take about ten 'pushes' to raise a standard block up one step of the Pyramid. Heavier stones would be handled by using more levers each having a shorter toe, thus producing less vertical lift at each operation, but more power.*

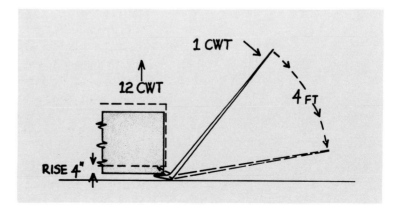

method which the Egyptians could have employed in their handling of these.

The first thing to realise is that the heavier stones are also larger stones and that this extra size allows more men to get round the load and work their levers. If the stones were the same breadth and height as the core stones, but very much longer, then the lifting ratios were unaltered and a stone twice as long only needed twice the number of levers. However, for stones of a greater sectional area or a denser material, (for example, the granite roof slabs to the King's Chamber of the Great Pyramid), the Egyptians would have had to develop a lever which was stronger in itself so that a greater ratio of thrust to lift could operate. A lever six feet long with a toe of only three inches could lift twice as much, especially with two men on the handle. Depending on the soundness of the levers, the 50 ton stones could have been raised by about 40 levers working together.

Because the angle of the pyramid sides exceeds 45° (or 'square pitch', as builders say) the flat part of the steps are narrower than the height of the blocks and, furthermore, it can be seen that the blocks themselves are generally wider than the steps, and would overhang the edge during jacking. The stones and the packing had therefore to be carefully balanced on the steps, but I am confident that experienced teams with practice would have had this risk well under control. The steps, however, would not have been wide enough to accommodate any stone larger than the standard core block, and no manual of pyramid building can be complete without a sound recipe for raising these very heavy stones. The key lies in the fact that these stones did not have to be raised above the halfway level of the structure, and thus a

Fig. 33 *Moving the largest stones. Wide steps could be formed temporarily to ease the handling of the heavier stones needed for the chamber roof and walls. The height of each step is determined by the general coursing of the core blocks but the extra width on each tread is obtained by omitting some of the stones at the edge of each course. The geometry of the pyramid is not impeded, and the missing stones can be inserted, starting from the bottom, when the heavy work is completed. This pyramid has already reached half its final volume.*

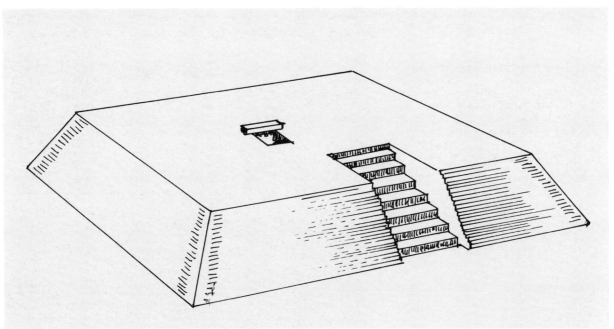

temporary set of 'building stairs' could be provided at a lower gradient and having much wider treads than the side of the pyramid. The drawing shows the basis of this temporary arrangement which would leave the other three sides free for raising the standard stones and could, after the need was over, be filled in with standard blocks, starting from the bottom (see fig. 33).

The greatest advantage to the builders in using levers for the whole building operation lay in the fact that there would have been no ramps or scaffolding cluttering up the area surrounding the growing pyramid. When the hauliers were working they could be accommodated on only three sides of the pyramid, thus leaving the fourth free for pedestrian access and the ground area in front of this side free for laying out the inevitable scatter of materials and stores indispensable for any building operation, large or small. The haulier teams would have passed the stones up the stepped sides in straight lines, side by side, using the whole width of the working platform: for example, at the halfway stage in height the top would have had a width of 240 feet, permitting about twelve teams to work at once. As the pyramid grew higher and the working platform narrower the number of teams would have needed to be reduced, but the spare men would have been available to make up for the greater height travelled by each of the teams remaining. The last few courses near the apex could have been served by only one team on each side of the pyramid. The diagram sets out the principle of this system (see fig. 34).

The standard core blocks might well have been put to other uses before they finally came to rest in the body of the pyramid. The previous explanations should have established the idea that the builders could easily handle these stones, which they would have classed as 'small' rather than 'large', and that they might well have moved them about from place to place to be used as

Fig. 34 *Many jacking lines. The working platform could have been supplied with stones from a large number of points simultaneously. The vertical lines represent 'jacking teams' passing the stones up the side of the pyramid. As the pyramid rose higher the men from the outer teams would join the centre ones, so that the same average number of men would always be employed.*

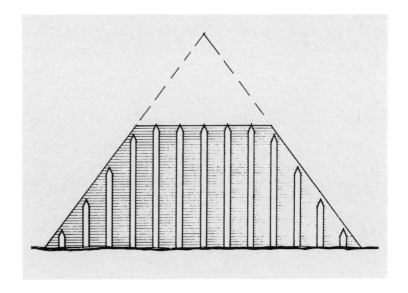

temporary scaffolding, perhaps, to help the men putting up the chamber stones. Timber must have been a scarce commodity compared with the free labour available and, if a temporary platform were needed for the masons to work on something above their reach, then it would have been a simple matter to bring up a few core stones for the purpose. If the heavy roof blocks over a chamber needed to have temporary support, then it would have been safer to stand some core blocks in the chamber rather than trust a flimsy timber scaffolding to take much weight. The blocks could well have become one of the general tools for the job, afterwards to play their part as an integral element in the permanent monument.

Their practice of developing to the utmost the materials and resources to hand suggests that the Egyptians were a race of conservative people who continued to improve what was known to them in preference to searching for new materials and techniques. The fact that they lived in a territory which supplied all their needs from within a fertile band of cultivation, and which was no more than a mile or two wide in places, may have affected their attitude towards progress. There may well have been a political or religious attitude which kept a restraining influence on initiative or original thought so that men were actively discouraged from new ideas. The Egyptians demonstrated their competence by the raising of the pyramids and other fine buildings, and yet they failed to recognise and exploit the full potentialities of the wheel or pulley until comparatively late in their history. A scaling ladder on wheels is shown in a relief dating from the Fifth Dynasty, but a thousand years later, tomb scenes show heavy stones and sculptures still being moved on sledges.[10] Sand is difficult for wheels to cope with, of course, and water transport was used extensively. Pulleys do not seem to have been known in Egypt until Roman times. Even on ships, ropes were passed over fixed wooden guides in such a way that the friction must have caused much heavy work for the sailors.[11]

On the building site the advanced use of levers may have overshadowed the occasional use of the roller: and, prior to the invention of the pulley, the builders would have been unlikely to recognise that a rope, lifting from above, could assist in a process which was done most naturally from beneath the load.

A lever could allow one man to do the work of twelve, so that the Egyptians had no cause to look any further for a better system of lifting the stones.

4 The craftsmen and their skills

The ability to raise the stone up to the working platforms was only one of many skills which the Egyptians needed if they were to build an accurate pyramid. The methods of lifting and the general organisation of movement described in my previous chapters would have allowed the builders to do no more than raise a shapeless stone mass, with rough stepped sides. The pyramid had to stand on a base which was square and level, and for this a basic command of measurement was essential. Later, to form an exact, smooth pyramid, not only the hand skills of the stonemasons were needed, but also their practical experience of shapes and solid geometry. It seems likely that the builders must have been confident before they started the Great Pyramid that they could finally produce a permanent, accurate pyramid shape, even though the work might take many years to complete and engage thousands of craftsmen and labourers.[1]

This chapter examines what we know of a mason's craft and the way in which he would have set about this work, because it was from his practical experience that all building developed. The skill of the craftsman's hands, coupled with his growing knowledge, were the ingredients which made it possible for the Egyptians to raise the pyramids and the other buildings and monuments which remain as a catalogue of their civilisation. It is possible for us in the twentieth century to come to a close understanding of how the Egyptian mason thought and worked, because both civilisations have used the same shaped hands and the same natural materials.

For six thousand years, up until the last century, the stonemason has been the principal contriver in the raising of large permanent buildings. His ability to cut stone into intricate shapes led to his mastery in the design of the complete building as, for example, in medieval times when men of his trade developed the Gothic cathedrals with graceful columns of great height, supporting fan vaulted ceilings of exact geometrical complexity. Such work did not have its origin in drawings prepared by laymen, but was conceived in detail by the masons who themselves worked the stone, using their exclusive knowledge of solid geometry and their acquired sense of structural stability. The masons considered themselves to be the superior craftsmen amongst the workers on a building site, keeping the secrets of their skills amongst themselves and training only those boys whom they might select, on a basis of family ties or privileged connection.

It is only a recent innovation that designers or architects should be regarded as professional people set apart from the craftsman by a training in theory at college or university. The designers whose work has stood for a thousand years or more were craftsmen themselves who had expanded their skills to the ultimate of a complete building. For instance, the great Italian architect Palladio was apprenticed to stonemasons in Vicenza at the outset of his career.

The stones which the Egyptian masons worked can provide, if we study them correctly, enough evidence to establish how the men had set about their tasks and how their skills had developed.

The length of the fertile Nile valley which gave such abundance of food also contained within its boundaries a variety of natural stones each suitable for a different purpose and the masons learnt how to make the tools which would best shape the material and leave it with an agreeable surface. The word 'tool' is intended in its widest sense, being either a forged metal, a piece of wood or a piece of harder natural material used as an abrasive or a polishing agent. The selection of stone available for building was similar to that in the British Isles and included limestones (varying from a soft, coarse grade to a finer hard material), sandstone, alabaster, and granites in different colours. Each type of stone had varieties of texture and colour according to its place of origin, or in some cases, its location within one particular quarry.

Many things relating to a mason's tools or his work have changed little during the last five thousand years. In the British Museum there is a small hand chisel dating from 3000BC,[2] but from its shape it might well have been borrowed from a mason's toolbag yesterday; except that the Egyptians used copper while today such tools are made of steel.* The disciplines of solid geometry have not changed and watching a mason converting a rough lump of stone into a polished cube is the best way of understanding the process of shaping a solid form, to any scale.

At the beginning the mason needs somewhere 'to start from' – some even plane that can be the basis of his progress from irregularity into order and geometrical form. Every block of natural stone has some sort of shape, and the line of the original strata in the quarry usually provides one reasonably flat surface which can be used as a starting point. This area must first be transformed into a precisely flat plane. The mason first chisels, or saws,[4] a channel, or pathway, along one edge of the surface and then works at this to get it 'plane' by testing it with a straight-edge; he calls this pathway a 'draft' – a beginning. He then cuts another along the opposite edge of the area and lays a straight-edge along each draft. Sighting across the two straight-edges will test whether the two drafts are in the same plane; if they are not he will say they are 'in twist' and will work at them until they are right.

*Ed: the Bronze Age in Egypt is generally regarded as beginning about 2000BC, (Middle Kingdom, Eleventh and Twelfth Dynasties), though rare specimens have been attributed to the Fourth and Fifth Dynasties.[3]

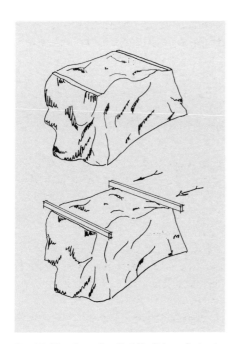

Fig. 35 *Flat channels called 'drafts' are first cut across opposite ends of a rough stone. These are the start of the first flat side and by sighting across the straight edges the mason can see if the drafts are parallel; if not, the edges are known as being 'in twist'. A joiner follows a similar principle when planing rough timber.*

Fig. 36 *A copy of a wall painting in the tomb of Rekhmara at Thebes. Although this is 1,000 years later than the Great Pyramid, it does show the basic principles of measuring and levelling being employed in a mason's workshop.*

This practice of sighting one edge against another is essential to the making of any plane or geometrical shape; a line of sight is more accurate than a piece of string. The joiner at his bench uses the principle when planing up a rough piece of wood by hand; he has two short winding sticks amongst his tools and by placing these across the plank at each end he can see whether the face is flat or 'winding'.

The mason now cuts the last two drafts so that he has a true 'rim' around his proposed plane, with raised virgin stone left in the middle. This is cut down ('bumped off') and the whole area smoothed over (see fig. 35).

A wall painting made about 1,000 years after the largest pyramids were built shows masons at their work (see fig. 36).[5] The bottom left drawing shows the centre being 'bumped off' and to test the plane the masons are using a set of boning rods and twine which is tightened between two of the rods while another of equal length is passed under the twine to test the stone for high places. The principle of this tool is important because it can be enlarged for full-scale levelling out on the site, substituting the line of sight for the twine and using rods about half the height of a man.

The mason must next inscribe on his plane surface four lines to make an exact square, and the painting shows the men checking this by measuring the diagonals, a common practice today in all trades; for example, every joiner keeps a batten fitted with a running slide with which he can check if window sashes are true after they have been cramped up. It is not the actual measured length which is important but the fact that the diagonals are equal. After this the stone is worked on all four sides and it is a skilled man indeed who can prove his cube by also checking the diagonals through the solid, using callipers. The slightest error will be exaggerated on the diagonal. My own first attempt needed so many corrections that the finished cube was only about half its intended size.

The study of a mason at work illustrated in the wall painting shows that the pyramid builders understood sighting, planes, squares, diagonals, and parallels, and that these skills could be enlarged for use on the building sites of the pyramids.

The Egyptians used angles other than right angles, in the battered wall faces and the sides of the pyramid; we would be able to understand their way of controlling these angles if we had not come to divide the circle into 360° and measure our own angles according to the 'spread' of the arms either side of the angle. Tradesmen generally, both in Ancient Egypt and today, assess their angles by the 'going' and the 'rise'; it is a more natural method and is more accurate on a large scale because there is no need for an enormous protractor.

Anyone walking past a building with a traditionally pitched roof under construction must have seen the carpenter climbing amongst the roof timbers and fixing together the rafters, ridges, hips and valleys. The angle-cuts at the ends of the timbers and the splays at the hips cannot easily be calculated arithmetically. A good carpenter cuts all these on the ground before assembling the roof but he has no use for a protractor; he most probably uses a 'steel square' which is a flat 'L' shaped steel rule with the arms 24 and 16 inches long and engraved with an apparently mystical series of sloping lines, scales and figures. His skill lies in deciding the pitch of the roof in terms of rise and going and applying this with a sense of solid geometry born of long experience. The mason makes his angles by 'measuring off'. If the roof, or pyramid is right, then the layman will accept and even admire it without having to be aware of its geometry; but if it is wrong, then the shape will offend the eye.

The mason at his banker creates a kind of portable datum on the stone and from this he measures his angles and distances, but on the building site he must establish a fixed datum which normally will be a level one. The word 'level' means a plane which is a tangent to the earth's surface, but a layman recognises a level area rather negatively as a place which has no slope. The Ancient Egyptians would have recognised this condition from their use of water in irrigation channels.* The Egyptians also knew how to set things in a vertical plane, that other important datum used by man and most usually established from a plumb-bob. However, a tradesman today can achieve great accuracy by the skilful use of a 'three foot level' which in fact sets up a right angle from the reading of a liquid at rest and trapped in a short glass phial.

It is simple, when setting upright something like a steel column, to hang the plumb line from the top, but the oldest problem of all is to use the plumb line to control a wall which is being built from the bottom upwards and the top of which does not exist. No doubt the earliest builders first plumbed up a temporary pole or batten and then built the wall up against it. In recent years a

*Ed: in the *JARCE*, XX, 1983, Mark Lehner reports on the holes and trenches found along the bases of the two largest pyramids. He discusses alternative proposals for the levelling of the bedrock floor (p. 14), and concludes that this must have depended on the use of water-filled troughs at each corner, the troughs being gradually extended towards the centre, to provide a water-levelled datum for the rock-levelling work, and the pavement laying. Lehner's proposal is more labour intensive than Peter Hodges', but is essentially similar; the existence of the actual trenches at each corner is in any case strong evidence that water was involved.

For further reading on Egyptian irrigation, see reference [6].

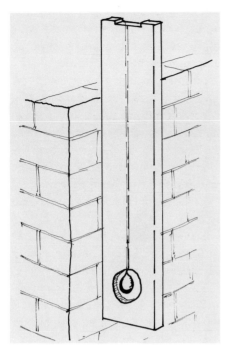

Fig. 37 *A normal plumb board with the string covering the centre line.*

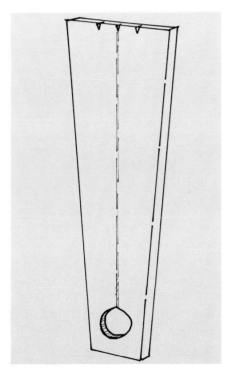

Fig. 38 *A board made wider at the top so that a battered wall face will be produced.*

Fig. 39 *A plumbing frame being used to obtain the correct pitch for the sides of the pyramid.*

gadget, known as Blakes Profiles, has been patented to help bricklayers to work on this ancient principle, and these are widely used on straightforward housing work. Before three foot levels were made the bricklayer and mason used a portable upright or plumb-board (see fig. 37); it needs to be held in one hand while the brick is tapped into position with the other. We can see by looking at the buildings around us that a skilled man can raise a corner, true and plumb for some two or three hundred courses. To obtain a battered face a special board is cut, as shown in the second drawing (see fig. 38).

A finished building can be admired for the accuracy of its shape and, in the case of a pyramid, for the equality of its angles, but this is merely the assessment of something which has been brought to exist and has no relation to the problem set for the builder who had to make the walls grow to a pre-determined shape. An analogy would be that of a man wishing to walk away from his starting point in a straight line. Normally he would fix his eye on some target ahead and, if he walks towards this, his steps must describe a straight line. However, if he must walk across a featureless desert, or into a thick fog, he will then be without an aiming point and he must make sure that every step he takes is made with reference to the preceding ones, and the new step must be in prolongation with these.

The pyramid builders could not have set up an aiming point in the sky and so they must have laid each course accurately in reference to the one below it (see fig. 39).

It is noticeable that the Ancient Egyptians did not have pairs of compasses amongst their tools – the full sized variety rather like those a teacher uses at the blackboard. It is not possible to inscribe an accurate arc with a piece of string, as you will discover if you

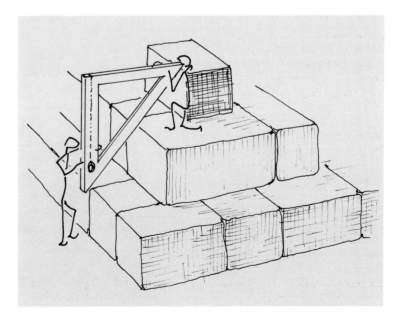

try it for yourself or watch a craftsman at his work. A rigid tool is essential. The Egyptians of the Third Dynasty seem to have overlooked the possibilities of the circle as these do not appear in any major structural form nor in such practical applications as the wheel or pulley. They were 'straight line men', their plans were laid out and their wall faces raised with strict regimentation that suggests they were a people whose natural inclination was to create an organised, disciplined and rather severe society.* The Arab of today, with over a thousand years of history in the Nile valley, exploits quite different skills; he is a freehand craftsman excelling in a fluid representation of line or form. The Ancient Britons excelled in the use of the circle and the gentle, smoothed form of earthwork embankments.

*Ed: some have argued that the Egyptians were aware of the concept of 'pi', but if we except the small attached columns and semicircular gables of the small solid tombs at Saqqara, these statements remain true of major structures.

5 Setting out a pyramid

The pyramid builders were people having the same practical capabilities as ourselves, working with similar materials and tools to those we still use today. Consequently, if they were able to raise the Great Pyramid then, so could we – you the reader and I, the writer – having studied and absorbed the principles involved, and given the necessary facilities. The more complicated geometry of the pyramid will be explained later, but at this stage enough has been offered to accomplish the essential task of setting out the base of the pyramid under the supervision of this mythical team of you and me, transported back through some 4,500 years in time.

I have had to make some reasoned assumptions as to how parts of the work would have been done, and these are discussed later in this chapter, as are my comments regarding possible social conditions and practices. In the meantime, let us pretend that we are living in the Fourth Dynasty at about 2550BC, that we have been appointed as principal contrivers of the projected pyramid and the task is ours to organise and complete the foundation work.

The modern archaeologist has the use of many scientific aids which can help him to discover and identify the relics of an earlier age but, amateur or professional, he must still cultivate that art of travelling backwards mentally, through time, and placing himself within the era which he is exploring. This use of an imaginary time machine is perhaps a discipline rather than an art, because it requires the time traveller to erase temporarily from his mind all his contemporary knowledge so that he can share the thoughts of the ancient people more clearly. This discipline is particularly necessary when we think about the pyramid builders, because we so often fail to appreciate that the loose term 'Ancient Egypt' covers a period of about 3,000 years. Many popular, and some serious, books on the subject have thrown together descriptions and photographs of buildings in such confusion that we may get the impression that everything happened almost at once.

It would be helpful to set the scene as the Great Pyramid is about to be started and thus place ourselves within the historic time scale. Our time machine has had to be guided backwards so as to pass through the last two-thirds of the Egyptian period until it reached a date during the reign of King Khufu, about 2550–2528BC. At this time the Egyptian civilisation had been in existence for about a thousand years and, having begun as two separate kingdoms of Upper and Lower Egypt, was now united and known as the 'Two Kingdoms'. The unification of the two kingdoms occurred some five hundred years before the Great Pyramid was started and our time machine was brought to a halt on the Giza cliffs. From this moment we should have to wait through a period of some thirteen hundred years (during which the temples at Karnak and the royal tombs in the Valley of the Kings were begun) before the reign of Rameses II, another one thousand years to the Ptolomaic period, and yet another two hundred and seventy odd years to the Roman period, due to end at 311AD.*

*Ed: authorities differ on dating, but these dates are in accordance with the *Atlas of Ancient Egypt*.[1] Opinions on the 'Two Kingdoms' theory are divided: Edwards endorses it completely,[2] whilst the *Atlas of Ancient Egypt*, p. 31, suggests that a more gradual period of unification was likely.

When we arrive we find that the Egyptians have become a highly organised society and, as part of their building capabilities, have mastered the quarrying and working of stone, the shaping of wood and copper and even the making of ropes, but not the development of wheel or pulley. They sometimes make use of rollers to assist the transport of heavy stones on sledges but for general handling and placing of the stones they have developed the use of the lever to a fine art.

We can now imagine ourselves to be inspecting the building site, a bare promontory of rock standing above the western edge of the fertile Nile valley. Here we are to build the largest and finest pyramid in the kingdom, destined to be the tomb for our pharaoh, Khufu, and the focus of continuing ceremonies which will ensure the fullness of his life in the afterworld and, consequently, the survival of our civilisation.

It is now about one hundred years since the first tall tomb mound was raised at Saqqara for the pharaoh Zoser. Up to this point there had been a continual evolution in tomb design, from the simplest form of burial pit to the covered type of tomb with a protective, inward sloping and flat-topped super-structure, incorporating compartments for the afterlife, and varying in size and splendour according to the status of the dead occupant: such a tomb was named after the 'mastabas', or low benches, which stood outside the Egyptian houses. This word 'mastaba' has never been superseded because there is nothing in general use today which quite repeats the distinctive shape, a completely functional form which consequently pleases the eye in its solid proportions.

Zoser's tomb marked a new stage: a modified mastaba base was enlarged outwards and upwards several times until the present shape of a bold 'stepped' pyramid emerged.[3] Since that time about six major pyramids have been built, but some of these were never finished. The last one to be completed was built for the last king, Sneferu, at the northern site at Dahshur, which is a place about twenty miles further up the river from here. Several of the masons with us now have worked on this structure at North Dahshur, which was completed in the true pyramid shape, the previous tomb built by Sneferu at South Dahshur having the blunted pyramid shape (the shape of the pyramid at Meidum, and the ruin of its outer mantle, is discussed in chapter 6). Sneferu's final tomb reproduces the upper pitch of the blunted pyramids and has become known amongst the workmen as the new Low Pyramid. The height is less than half the base so that the sides run up at less than square pitch.

The base was large at about 720 feet and the men now find it hard to believe that, although at Giza we are going to increase the base by only 1/20th in length up to 756 feet, the new pyramid with steeper sides will use almost twice as much material. This pyramid for King Khufu will stand nearly half as high again as the Low Pyramid and, being set on this cliff overlooking the valley, will be seen for all time as the greatest ever built.

Every pharaoh wishes to secure his afterlife by having his embalmed body laid to rest in the finest possible tomb but, as he cannot with confidence entrust this task to his successor, he must build the tomb during his own lifetime and leave access for the later insertion of the body. This makes calls upon the builders to use much labour and ingenuity in the contrivance of secret chambers and passages with thief-proof sealing devices (which may nevertheless be penetrated by later generations of tomb robbers). If a pharaoh could rely on his successor to build the tomb, then the body with its attendant deposit of gold and jewels could be interred first and afterwards covered with an impenetrable tomb constructed without any passages or entrances. A pharaoh will leave an endowment to maintain the priests and the tomb guards after his death.*

Whilst we stand on this open site watching the arrival of the men and their families, there is a moment before the start of a busy routine to consider the wider implications of our task. We are faced on one hand by the political pressures which demand a rapid completion of the pyramid, and on the other by the daunting thought that this is to be the largest structure that man has ever built. When buildings are in the dreaming, practical limitations take a backward place, but we have accepted the responsibility of producing a completed pyramid, because nothing less will serve the purpose.

The preceding years have accumulated a valuable reserve of experience but, nevertheless, each project contains within its conception the seeds of failure, and we must be watchful that they do not germinate. However many times we may make a building we always begin with hope and enthusiasm, and for us who start this work by physically marking out the extent of our intentions, this is a unique moment.

Decisions as to the general position and the size of the pyramid have already been taken in the light of current religious thinking in the Kingdom and within the limitations of the terrain and the materials available. The site has already been examined and tested by the masters of quarries in the neighbourhood and their knowledge of the underlying strata has helped them to verify that a firm rock base exists to take the great weight which is to be superimposed. The work on the ceremonial approach causeway from the Nile has already started,[5] and we on this site must begin to level the rock surface and then mark out the exact square of the pyramid.

We have at our disposal a starting gang of about two thousand men with their women and children, all of whom live in villages of mud huts which have been erected close to the site. They are provided with the usual basic foods and other supplies which enable them to make their own domestic arrangements.

These numbers include some master masons to supervise the setting out, some working masons and a large number of labourers. The masons live in their own village, considering themselves to be superior in rank and skill to the other workers and requiring better houses and standards of living. The farmers and the labourers who cultivate the fields have come to resent the ever-growing numbers of masons who have to be supported by a levy made on the crops grown in the valley. The Pharaoh's work must be maintained and there are now more masons than priests to be provided for, while at the same time the use of stone is prohibited to the general population who must construct their houses of mud bricks. All the quarrying of stone is controlled by the state to ensure a regular supply for the royal palaces and tombs.

The main core stones are already beginning to arrive from the quarry, and these will have to stand around the outside of the site during the three or four months it will take to prepare the ground. Nothing must be brought on to the actual site which may get in the way of our sight lines.

The astronomers have told us the approximate position of the pyramid and its general direction, so that we can start by preparing a level strip of ground on which they can precisely indicate the position, bearing and length of one side, basing this on their observations of the sun and the stars. We know that this is to be about 750 feet long. The general lie of the land suggests that a level bed can be obtained by cutting down some of the base rock where it is standing too high, but it is not too much to be unreasonable. The work must start from the lowest point of the solid rock, as the pyramid cannot stand securely on any made-up ground, nor on a rock stratum which is sloping.

We will call this first side of the pyramid the 'base line', and to lay this out exactly we first need a levelled broad track across the rock about 6 feet wide and extending at least 50 feet beyond each end of the base line. Starting at the lowest end we cut the first 100 feet or so roughly level and then build on this rock a water channel about 1 foot wide and 50 feet long; this work is best done by a team of farmers, or 'drowners', from the valley, who will use their irrigation skills in building a temporary canal, which will retain the water that they bring up from the Nile. We now set two stones firmly in the water, one at each end of the canal, so that their top surfaces are flush with the surface of the water, and on these the masons will stand their boning rods. These rods are made exactly equal in length (about 4 feet) and with a flat top. The men who sight along the tops of these two rods are then sighting in a level plane and their line of sight extends beyond the canal over the whole length of the base line. At the same time other men hold rods of the correct length on the virgin ground and the 'sighters' can then judge whether the ground is high or low. There is no need to extend the canal along the whole length of the base line, and the line of sight itself will be level provided that the stones have been carefully set (see figs 40 and 41). The actual length is decided upon according to the conditions of the site, but the best position is usually at the corner of the square so that the same datum stone serves for two adjacent sides.

Fig. 40 *A levelling canal in use. The man standing and sighting across the tops of the boning rods is out of the picture, and behind us. The two levelling stones are set with their top surface flush with the water, one at each end of the canal. The farthest rod is standing on virgin ground and the sighter can tell whether this ground is higher or lower than the levelling datum.*

Fig. 41 *Levelling the base. Using three 'boning rods' to test the levels of the ground. The rods are of equal length; one man sights across the top of two held upright in a short water channel, giving a level line of sight against the third rod held on the ground to be levelled, which may be as far as 300ft distant.*

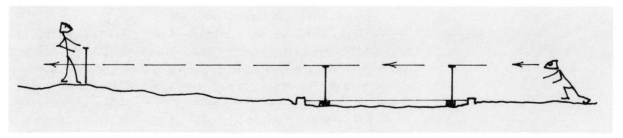

Cutting down the surface of the virgin rock is hard work, as the men must kneel or squat to chisel at the ground between their feet. The finer class of mason spurns this hard graft and leaves it to the apprentices and the less skilful amongst the masons' families. Now is the moment for the priests and the astronomers to fix the position of the base line and for us to mark permanently the two end positions, and also the centre. The astronomers will most likely fix on the centre point of the base line first and from this set out the centre axis of the pyramid running true north. From this axis we can square off to give the base line and then work out the remaining lines for the enclosing square. This whole square must be marked out before any building can begin.

Setting out a right-angle presents no problem to us provided the work is done carefully and without undue haste. It is necessary to extend the base line beyond the corner point so that one is working with both angles in a letter 'T', and not just the one right-angle. The point where the angle is to be set is carefully marked on the ground and the lines are stretched out with cord at least fifty feet in each direction, and pegged out as nearly as possible to a right-angle as the eye can judge. We then make three marks, one along each line at an exact equal distance from the meeting point, measure each hypotenuse and adjust the line slightly until each is precisely equal (see fig. 42). Provided the measurements are

Fig. 42 *Diagram to show the most accurate way to set out a right angle on the ground. The base line must be extended beyond the corner point.*

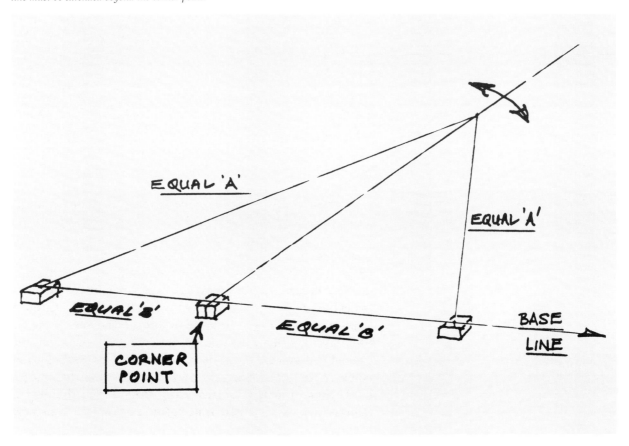

carefully checked and the marks are at least 50 feet out from the intersection, then the angle will be a good one. We can make a further check later during the setting out process.

The end marks for the base line will have been cut into the rock, but almost immediately we must firmly set up sighting stones, placed away from the corners but in line with the base sides, so that when the ground corner marks are covered by the new masonry we can re-create the base lines by sighting between these posts. Every builder does this when he builds a house or a walled enclosure, but he uses temporary boards fixed to pegs and calls them 'profile boards' (see fig. 43).

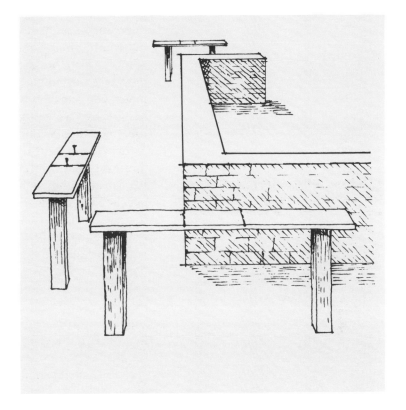

Fig. 43 *Marking the base. A builder erects 'profile boards' opposite the end of each wall, because pegs driven into the ground to mark each corner will be lost when the building work starts. Similarly, the pyramid builders must have placed firm markers to record the base line throughout the whole building period.*

Our next task is to mark out along the base line the exact length of the pyramid side. This must be done in such a way that the length can be recorded and then repeated exactly for the other three sides, but any builder will tell you that to measure such a length is much more difficult than you might think. A long rope or twine is quite useless over a length of some 750 feet, as it can easily be stretched several feet by hard pulling; it will even creep as the moistness in the air changes through the day. There has been talk of making a large drum and rolling this along the ground,[6] but this is a clumsy process and the drum tends to jump on the rocky ground and sometimes slip when the men pull too hard. There is only one satisfactory method and this merely requires two wooden measuring rods to be made, each about 20 feet long and shod at each end with a metal cap; these caps can then be filed until the rods are exactly the same length. The secret is to lay the first rod down flat and have it held firmly in position while the second is laid end to end, with the metal caps just touching. The second is held down while the first is lifted and laid so as to touch the other end of the second one, and so on down the line. Provided that the wood has been well seasoned and the rods are carefully handled there can be no room for error. It is dangerous to use only one rod and to make a mark at the end before moving it forward, because the thickness of this mark is added to the length at each move.

Being aware of all the difficulties, the work will be carefully done, marks cut in the rock and profile stones set up opposite the marks. The rods we use may be needed for checking the measurements later, so we shall store them safely away, otherwise they may finish up as fire wood – the certain destiny of any loose pieces of wood on a building site.

Now that we have made one straight level line as a start, we must continue with two more lines at right-angles from the corners so as to form the next two sides of the square. We set up approximate angles at each corner and repeat the process with water canals and boning rods to form the wide bands of levelled ground. The canals this time are started at each end of the base line so that the new lines will be at the same level. When the ends of the next two sides are joined across we shall have, on a greatly enlarged scale, the four drafts which a mason cuts on his stone as the perimeter of his first fair plane. But our plane has to be not only flat but also level, so we must therefore continue the levelling process all round, when the boning rods on the last canal should, in theory, sight back on the datum stone laid down in the first canal. If it is at all possible to clear the centre of the site then we shall measure the diagonals of our square, because this will give us the final confirmation that our work has been correctly done.

This is the time when the officials from the Court keep calling on the site to complain that there is so little to show for our efforts, thousands of men at work but not one stone laid above the ground; we try to explain that only a true base can make a true pyramid. In any case, we say, someone may come along in another few thousand years' time and check our measurements, and we want them to see that we knew how to do a job well.

The edges of our square may now be true and level but we are left with large areas of virgin rock standing in the middle, and it seems a wasteful process to cut all this away and then replace it with imported stone blocks, using much time and effort. However, we know from the experience of earlier generations that the pyramid must stand firm and, in particular, there must be no room for any stones to move sideways inside the core, because this will cause a settlement in the higher stones of the pyramid. With this in mind we inspect the higher parts of the ground, clear away any unstable material and level off the tops of the remainder so that the new core blocks will each have a firm level base on which to stand. It needs no more than common sense to see that if the raised centre is left with sloping sides there will be a tendency for the core blocks to slide downwards and outwards and encourage the pyramid to burst out at the sides near the bottom. Each core block in the lower courses will have to bear an enormous weight, and we cannot go back later inside the pyramid to replace any which move or are crushed. We are preparing the ground to support a tomb which will stand for ever; no human being will set eyes again on the rock which we have levelled to receive the masons' work.

At this stage we can take stock of our progress and look ahead a little into the future. With the coming of the next flooding of the Nile there will be several thousand labourers available to act as hauliers, some on our building site and others at various stages of the journey from the quarry. They also will live in village communities and work in family teams. Although the work is hard there will be intense competition between these teams as to which can give the best service and make the greatest contribution to the Pharaoh's tomb. The men become highly skilled in their work from the practice they obtain each year and they show great pride in handling such loads as would appear impossible to someone such as a fisherman or a scribe.

With the setting out and the ritual foundation ceremonies completed we can leave the site, return to the twentieth century and then examine some of the suggested working methods and find out how they compare with modern practice.

My remarks describing the social status of the masons and the living arrangements for all the men were intended as a reasonable fiction rather than an historical fact. It has been the custom throughout the ages, until recently, that a man and his family should live on top of the workshop. Work has always commanded a craftsman's attention from dawn to dusk and has been something inseparable from the support of family life. That the masons may have set themselves apart is pure conjecture, although it was certainly the practice throughout medieval times, and it may help if one realises that the Egyptian master mason was the equivalent of today's senior civil engineer. The idea of the productive worker having to support the government employee is one known to us all.

The fact that the rock surface under the Great Pyramid was brought down to a level plane can be established by looking at the site today and noting that the bottom course has purposely been set level. Surveyors have marvelled at the degree of accuracy which the Egyptians achieved and this establishes clearly for me that they must have worked from the datum of a liquid at rest and, as they were efficient and orderly workers, they must have used the most economical method which could be devised.

The observance of a liquid at rest is still the most accurate method of determining the level plane, and none of the modern measuring techniques based on electronics or radio waves have superseded this simple phenomenom.* The surveyor using to-day's levelling instruments is most likely to be reading from a datum of the bubble in a spirit level enclosed within his level or theodolite (see fig. 44), and in no case will the liquid in the vial be any longer than the palm of a man's hand. There are some modern instruments which work from the datum of a short pendulum but both systems are relying on the same states of nature that were used by the Ancient Egyptians. They did not have the sophistication of the sealed spirit and air bubble but they can only have achieved the accuracy they did by the use of a

*Ed: this was written in 1978.

Fig. 44 *A surveyor using a modern theodolite. This instrument can be adjusted to read the line of sight to within one 180th part of one degree by setting the bubble in a spirit-filled glass vial no more than 3in long.*

liquid at rest; and from their life in the Nile Valley, depending on irrigated water, it is sound reasoning to assume that they were skilful in the control of water levels. There is no evidence which supports the use of the canals I have suggested,* but such a design is the one most likely to have been evolved by craftsmen having the other related skills.

Several authorities, including Somers Clarke,[7] have suggested that a large site such as a pyramid base was levelled by flooding over the entire area with water and, further, that the slight inaccuracy in the base of the Great Pyramid came about because a breeze was blowing at the time the work was done. Such a method on this scale would have been wasteful and quite impracticable, for several reasons. Firstly, it was improbable that such large areas of virgin rock bed would not have had several fissures causing continuous leaks; secondly, having flooded the area the men would have found it impossible to work on the rock surface under the water which would be constantly disturbed by hundreds of men threshing about; such a method would have seemed wasteful and inefficient to such excellent builders.

The Egyptians' understanding of the 'line of sight' is inherent in their achievements. The straight walls, the even gradients and level courses of their construction work over some five centuries could not have been done without sighting one thing against another. The practice is natural to builders and engineers dealing with practical elements.

The procedure I have outlined for laying out the right-angles is one which any builder would use who did not have an optical square or a theodolite to hand. Extending the base line beyond the corner so that one forms a pair of right-angles will give the most accurate result.

Measuring out a long distance using two rods alternately is a practice often used by builders' foremen today when a steel tape is not available. The linen tapes are not reliable and the pencil marks made at each laying of a single rod can add up to an error of 1 inch in 100 feet.

The most likely error to occur when using a pair of rods is that the surveyor will lose count of the number of times the rods had been laid down. It is surprisingly easy on a long line to get into a muddle and forget whether it was the last or the next rod which is, say, the seventeenth measure. A surveyor's chain is always sold with ten loose marking pins so that one can be put into the ground at each measure; for the same reason a cricket umpire keeps six pebbles to be transferred, one at a time, out of one pocket into the other as each ball is bowled. I have no doubt that the Egyptians must have devised something similar when measuring a long line.

The suggestion that the rods had to be kept for the duration of the building is based on the fact that the standard Egyptian measure varied from time to time, so that it would have been necessary to determine measuring standards at the start of a large project. This would have enabled measurements to be communicated around the site and out to the quarries.

In order to communicate the size of anything, be it a piece of ground, a building or a block of stone, it is essential to convert this size into dimensions which will be readily understood. Such a scale of measurement is thus a language evolved through necessity. It is in fact the oldest of the languages that have been in use continually; it is older than the hieroglyphs and yet we can read it and understand its construction because we ourselves use a similar one in the twentieth century. The fact that cubits, palms and digits are not far removed from yards, feet and inches discloses the essence of any good scale language, namely that there must be a convenient unit to describe anything in common use from the largest to the smallest. Ideally the units will allow measurements to be expressed by a figure which does not far exceed the ten fingers on our two hands. A successful scale must be made up of what I call 'units of convenience' in the same way that a verbal language is built up from the basic messages which are essential to the conduct and survival of any community.

Herodotus tells us, for example, that the Egyptians of his time described the length of a coastline or the size of vast estates in 'schoeni', smaller estates in 'parasangs', the estates of the not so poor in 'stades', and of the poor in 'fathoms'.[8] It has been shown that the builders of the time, working to a smaller scale, used cubits, palms and digits. The British 'imperial' system once offered us miles, furlongs, chains, yards, feet and inches; the last named being easily divided by successive halving until a suitable size of unit was achieved, ie., a half inch, a quarter inch, an eighth inch, etc.

Regretfully, we in Great Britain are doomed by political decree to abandon a scale prolific with units of convenience and adopt Napoleon's metric scale which has none. The methods laid down by the so-called experts as to how the scale is to be used in my own trade has resulted in a plethora of useless noughts and the ridiculous circumstance whereby the only permitted unit of convenience is so small that it must be communicated by thousands to describe the height of an ordinary door. The experts could not have realised that a scale is a language and that the units of convenience are its syntax.

According to Petrie,[9] the Royal cubit used at the time of the Great Pyramid measured 20.62 inches and was sub-divided into seven palms, each of four digits. If these units derived from the size of man's fore-arm and hand, then a picture emerges of men with rather long arms and narrow hands. Other cubits used during the subsequent 3,000 years of Egyptian history have been found varying from 20.1 inches to 20.67 inches.

It is interesting to speculate as to whether the Egyptians were able to calculate in advance the volume of the Great Pyramid and express this in practical units. I have not found quoted anywhere documentary evidence contemporary with this period that establishes their capability to do this, and I cannot imagine that they dealt in formulae based on base areas and height.*

*Ed: the Rhind Papyrus does show their familiarity with calculating volumes relevant to pyramids.

No builder today would start a project without first calculating the quantities of materials to be used, but few, if any, of us could do this for a pyramid without resorting to a book of tables. The Egyptians however may not have thought it necessary to have this information in advance, and may have done no more than assess one pyramid by the size of the previous one. My comment earlier in this chapter is by way of a hint that the eventual volume of the Great Pyramid may have taken them by surprise. The task is for the archaeologists to find evidence of contemporary calculations, but if I myself were asked to calculate such a volume I could only do it on a practical comparison with a model; perhaps the Egyptians did just the same, using a scale model made up of small blocks.

Fig. 45 *Photograph to give scale to Zoser's buttress Pyramid at Saqqara (usually known as the Step Pyramid). The figures are standing in the concourse area in front of the south face; one of the restored temples which adjoined the east perimeter wall can be seen at the right of the picture.*

Fig. 46 *The north-east angle at Saqqara – the author is standing in front of the ruins of the lowest buttress.*

6 The anatomy of the pyramids

Exploring the full range of interest that can be found in the pyramids involves much more than just calculating how the stones could have been man handled up the sides of the Great Pyramid. The most rewarding discovery lies in recognising the moment when the builders first tried out a new system of building which would later lead them to construct the greatest pyramids in the world. This moment did not come at the beginning, when they raised a 'step' pyramid at Saqqara, but after the completion of a similar structure at Meidum. The change in the working practices of the masons and the widening of their achievements can be seen and understood by examining the anatomy of the stonework – that is to say, the shape and size of the stones, their relative positioning, and the particular role which each was intended to fulfil (see figs 45 and 46).

The main thread of development can be represented by six of the principal pyramids which are still standing today; these are shown in my table 3 (p. 54) and can be listed as follows:

No.	Common names	Location	Reigning King	Dynasty
1	Zoser's Stepped	Saqqara	Zoser	Third
2	Meidum	Meidum	Huni or Sneferu	Fourth
3	Blunted Bent	Dahshur	Sneferu	Fourth
4	Red Low	Dahshur	Sneferu	Fourth
5	Khufu's Cheop's The Great The First	Giza	Khufu	Fourth
6	Khafre's Chephren's The Second	Giza	Khafre	Fourth

We are not concerned here primarily with the historical background but more with the masonry itself; this is so outstanding in its quality that it forms a remarkable monument to the masons' skill. It is important to remember that the structures were built within a span of only two centuries and that a continuous chain of advancing skill was passed on through successive generations of stone masons. A man in growing from boyhood to old age might well have helped with three of the pyramids.

Table 3

LOCATION & BUILDER	DYNASTY		AVERAGE STONE WEIGHTS	
			CORE	FACINGS
SAQQARA KING ZOSER	III		¼–½ ton	½ ton
MEIDUM COMPLETED BY KING SNEFERU	IV		1½ tons	1½ tons
DAHSHUR 'BLUNTED' PYRAMID KING SNEFERU	IV		2–3 tons	3 tons
DAHSHUR 'LOW' PYRAMID KING SNEFERU	IV			
GIZA THE GREAT PYRAMID KING KHUFU	IV		2½ tons	4 tons
GIZA KING KHAFRÉ	IV		2–3 tons	6 tons

APPROX. SCALE   0   100   200   METRES

I was attracted to studying the practical aspects of the evolution after reading several propositions, of apparent authority, that the Blunted Pyramid had acquired its shape because the builders had run out of the time or the confidence to continue the steep lower sides up to an apex.[1] If this were true, then these builders had displayed the testing of their human competence, as it were, to destruction and an event like this could explain something of their methods of working. But I was not convinced by the reasoning (where, indeed, any such is put forward) behind these propositions, and there is not a scrap of evidence to support them. An examination through fresh eyes might show that there existed a number of impracticable theories about the building of the pyramids, and that these, having advanced in some cases from surmise to apparent fact only through frequent repetition, should now be discarded.

Stone seems to have been first used to face the sides of a tomb at the mastaba nucleus of Zoser's Step Pyramid at Saqqara.[2] By

Fig. 47 *A low wall built of squared stones bonded together.*

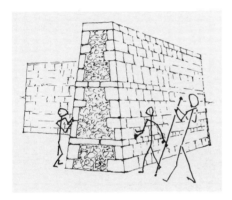

Fig. 48 *A high wall must have greater thickness. The better, harder stones are used only on the outside, while the centre is made up of small rough stones and weak mortar.*

Fig. 49 *The lower portion of this early buttress at Saqqara is built of squared stones laid with very little mortar. Two metre rod.*

that time the masons, who were already long experienced in the building of stone walls, knew that the mound would be more safely contained if the walls leaned inwards (see figs 47 and 48). Engineers would call these 'retaining walls' but a more convenient term is 'buttress' or 'buttress walls'. When it was decided to add height to the tomb the builders recognised that the new, higher walls would themselves need to be buttressed otherwise they would burst outwards. Thus the shape of the 'Step' or 'Buttress Pyramid' resulted, to be repeated at the Unfinished Pyramid of Sekhemkhet at Saqqara, others at Zawiet el Aryan, and the pyramid at Meidum, (disguised by an outer mantle). The anatomy of these tombs is readily discovered but from this point onwards, I maintain that historians or archaeologists who have assumed that all pyramids are buttress pyramids (for example,[3]) have misread the available evidence.

I introduce the generic term 'buttress pyramid' to define all those pyramids, irrespective of their outer shape, which were built on the principle just described. I believe that this particular term is necessary to make a distinction from the different type of pyramid which will be described as 'coursed'. The term 'accretion face' used by some previous writers is not sufficient to identify the vital purpose of the buttress.

In examining the tombs listed in my sequence (table 3), I propose to select only those details which speak of workmanship or the personal achievement of the masons. The exact sizes of the stones will not always be given because such exactness would be a distraction; many earlier observers became so engrossed in precise dimensions that they missed much of the information which the pyramids can offer about the masonry practices of the Ancient Egyptians. It is the pattern and the average which can best inform us in these matters.

Looking first at Zoser's Pyramid, we can see that some of the earlier work (see fig. 49) is made up like a masonry wall with

squared stones closely laid in definite courses with very little, if any, mortar between them. The stones vary in size but the largest (2ft x 1ft x 1ft 3ins) weighs not more that three hundredweight. Later, to construct the outer buttresses, the masons have used much larger stones but at the same time have made a saving in labour by not squaring the unseen faces. As each subsequent pyramid came to be built, the stone weight was increased and the quality of the dressing improved (see fig. 50). The headers in the later face work at Zoser's weigh about half a ton each and are laid in level courses with a mixture of headers and stretchers. These latter have been the first to fall out, while the predominating headers, with their tails bedded in a core of mortar, have stayed in place, thus delaying further collapse (see fig. 51).

At the outer face the stones were only roughly squared so that a wide mortar joint was left exposed to the erosive winds. The design of the quoins (corner stones) was not given any special attention, with the result that the entire pyramid is being slowly torn away at the angles (see fig. 52). These faults are important to note because later work shows that the masons had displayed a mastery of their trade by correcting these faults long before the consequences could have been very obvious.

Fig. 50 *The south face at Saqqara with earlier work superimposed by a later enlargement. During the interval the masons had learnt to lay their stones in even courses and to handle stones of consistently greater weight. Two metre rod.*

Fig. 51 *Detail of south-east angle, Saqqara. The sand-bearing wind has eroded the mortar from between the stones, laid in alternate courses of headers and stretchers. The corner stones are the first to fall away from the structure. Six courses equal the height of a man.*

Fig. 52 *Zoser's Pyramid disintegrating from the angles.*

The next in my sequence is the partly ruined buttress pyramid at Meidum (see figs 53–7), and by examining its masonry faces an observer should be able to tell at once that it could not have been built immediately following upon Zoser's. The jump in both stone size and workmanship is too great to have been achieved without some intervening experience and this was most probably gathered at the unfinished pyramids mentioned above. The Meidum buttresses display masonry work of the finest quality; the face stones weigh up to one-and-a-half tons each, they are exactly laid and neatly jointed, the masonry faces are truly plane and the external angles as straight and precise as any man or machine could achieve today.

Meidum face work set a pattern which was to be followed throughout the Fourth Dynasty; it is a pattern which was designed on the basis of good masonry practice, namely to show the minimum of joints exposed to the weather and to provide the greatest durability at the angles of the structure. The longest available stones were laid as stretchers; the quoins, built up of the very best, selected, stones were of great length bonded alternately so as to lace together the external angles. The stretchers have a length up to four times the course thickness so that they measure about 7ft x 1ft 10ins thick x 1ft 9ins deep. Most of those stones which appear as the shortest on elevation (about one-and-a-half times course thickness) are headers which project back into the core. Those parts of the masonry which were intended to be shielded from the weather by an outer buttress were built of stones of only slightly lesser weight but without the same precision of jointing.

Meidum is the last buttress pyramid in my sequence. A hole which was opened up on the north face enables us to study how the masonry technique was developing before the next and vital change in the progression was brought about. My photographs (see figs 56 and 57) show the pattern of the face work and in particular the stretcher course above the hole, where four stones had been so tightly fitted that they came to form a flat unsupported arch some 28 feet long against all the laws of structure. The seven courses of rough-hewn face work, showing on either side of the hole, had been laid on top of the finished buttress when the structure was enlarged with an outer set of concentric buttresses, one of which appears above the band of rough hewn stones. The equality of the standards of work below and above this band demonstrates that the enlargement must have been an immediate succession onto the earlier pyramid. The competence of the masons may have grown steadily year by year, but the standard of face work laid down at the start of a pyramid seems to have been followed throughout its construction, whether this lasted for five years or twenty five.

Fig. 53 *The partly ruined buttress pyramid at Meidum viewed across the desert under rare winter rain clouds. The structure, which was raised within the century subsequent to Saqqara, still stands 230ft above the desert floor. The modern barrack buildings can be seen in front of the heap of collapsed material. The steep unsupported faces rise some 100ft above the mound.*

Fig. 54 *The east face of Meidum, which overlooks the Nile valley and faces away from the eroding sand-bearing winds of the desert.*

Whilst the face work pattern may show a consistency throughout its evolution, the core structure underwent a purposeful and essential change. By the time that Meidum was built the masons were using core stones almost as large as those in the face, but they were only roughly hewn and had all been laid as headers, in mortar, without the coursing and bonding which would have formed a stable core. The stones are without any bonding into the buttresses behind them and if the face work is removed, then the core must collapse.

It has often been written, that Meidum was afterwards enclosed to form the first true pyramid,[4] and that this outer mantle collapsed at some later time. Many sectional drawings have also appeared but it was most probably Petrie, in a folio of 1892

Fig. 55 *The north-west angle of Meidum from a closer view point. The bands of rougher stone were originally covered by outer buttresses.*

Fig. 56 *The hole in the north face of Meidum showing the division between the roughly hewn core stones and the facing stones which rise approximately 1ft 10ins each course. The hole is about 40ft long and 25ft high.*

Fig. 57 *To give a scale to the masonry I have superimposed a London bus in outline.*

*Ed: the base has recently (1987) been partly exposed.

(*Medum*, published London), who first promoted speculation into fact by drawing a true pyramid shape above the mound. The lower part of the mantle does still exist at a pitch of about 52° but is hidden within the rubble mound enclosing the base;* however, there is no evidence as to the original shape of the mantle at the summit. If the structure had been completed I would suggest that it is more likely that the shape would have been that of a blunted pyramid, similar to the one which was to follow. The rubble mound may be no more that the 'leavings' of sand and small stones from a demolition rather than the result of some dramatic collapse.

The best drawing of the mantle is that by A. Rowe.[5] This shows that the core was made up of stones similar to those within the buttresses but with the essential difference that they were laid horizontally and not at right angles to the face. This marks a further step in the evolution. Rowe does not show if the stones were coursed or bonded, neither does he detail the lower face stones of the mantle.

The 'Blunted' or 'Bent' Pyramid at Dahshur (see fig. 58) occupies a key place in the sequence because its construction shows that the builders were reaching the peak period of their growing competence and had now evolved, without any outside influence, the vital change in technique which allowed them to exploit the true pyramid form and raise larger, and again larger structures, each of enduring stability.

Fig. 58 *The Bent Pyramid at Dahshur showing the scale and construction of the casing stones. Also known as the Blunted Pyramid.*

The key may be recognised from a study of the exposed core, which can be seen as being more stable than that at Meidum. The stones are squared top and bottom and they are bonded together horizontally. The two pyramids have the same face pattern but this is not evidence that buttresses exist inside both of them. The face stones lie at an angle to the pitch but this only follows earlier practice with buttresses and leaning walls. It is the coursing of the core which is the innovation: the face stones have become attachments to the structure and the manner of their laying no longer affects the stability of the pyramid. The builders appear to have realised that any buttress faces within the structure would have formed planes of weakness and that this danger could be avoided by bonding the core stones together, right through from face to face of the pyramid. We would do this ourselves, almost by instinct; if given a box of model bricks with which to build a pyramid, we would not start by forming buttresses but by laying the bricks flat in layers, starting from a square base.

It is a further fact that the forming of any buttresses would have protracted the operation and made it unnecessarily difficult.

The pattern of face work at Meidum is repeated at the Blunted Pyramid but the scale has been enlarged so that the course thickness is about 2 feet 9 inches and the stone weights proportionately greater. The magnificent size and quality of the quoins in the lower slopes continues into the upper part of the structure, refuting any suggestion that this part was built with any less care. The theory that the upper pitch was lowered as an expediency has no substance. If the masons had been forced to truncate the pyramid during progress then they would most likely have chosen a much lower pitch for the top – no more than was needed to create a 'fall' across the top surface.

Despite the vast scale of the three pyramids attributed to Sneferu, and of those started by his son and grandson, they were all completed.

The next pyramid in my sequence stands at northern Dahshur and is generally known as the 'Red Pyramid' (see fig. 59), but I prefer to use the word 'Low' because of its lower pitch. The pitch of the sides is only about 43°, an angle close to that of the upper 'Blunted' and also to the gradient of the hips of the two largest pyramids at Giza. It is a mistake however to be diverted into a study of mere coincidences; it is enough to note that this coursed

Fig. 59 *The Low, or Red Pyramid at Dahshur, showing that the pitch of the sides is lower than that of other pyramids.*

pyramid is the first structure to display the true pyramid form. It has been stripped of its face work and the edge of the core shows that the stones were laid in rigidly defined level courses.

Building activities next moved to Giza where the Great Pyramid built by Khufu displays the typical pattern of a coursed pyramid (see fig. 60). The average core-stone weight has now reached some two-and-a-half tons but there are considerable variations in the course thicknesses, beginning from a base course 5 feet thick and reducing gradually through the next five courses until the average of 3 feet is reached (see fig. 61). Above this the variations appear not to follow any logical pattern and may have been decided according to the thickness of the natural beds in the quarries.

There is a deep incursion into the southern face (see fig. 62) but this does not reveal any inner buttress face as should be the case if the drawing made by Borchardt,[6] had been a factual one (see fig. 63). This sectional drawing is very common and appears in many more books than those I have listed.[7] It was never claimed by its author to be more than a speculation and was based on the mistaken idea that a pyramid could only be constructed around a buttress core. If this buttress method had never been used by the Ancient Egyptians but they had begun instead by raising simple, small pyramids the coursed method would have been taken for granted and Borchardt would never have made his drawing.

There are references to 'girdle stones',[8] or 'large blocks of stone',[9] which are said to occur at regular intervals in the ascending

Fig. 60 *Khufu's Great Pyramid – the south face, showing the distinct lines of level coursing.*

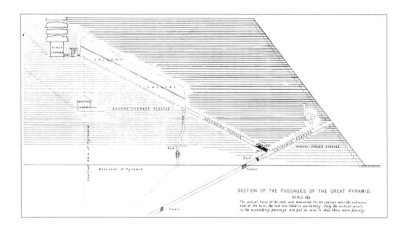

Fig. 61 *Petrie's drawing showing the Great Pyramid passages: note the omission of any direct reference to the supposed 'accretion faces'.*

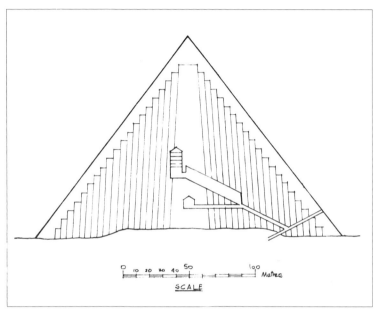

Fig. 63 *A cross-section drawing through the Great Pyramid showing the lines of the 'accretion faces' conjectured by Borchardt as having been the method of construction. This drawing is frequently reproduced although there is no hard evidence to support such a theory.*

Fig. 62 *The lower half, about 120 courses, of the Great Pyramid; the south face at sunset. The large hole is the result of the incursion of earlier archaeologists, convinced that the pyramids were hollow and contained vast stores of priceless treasures.*

passage of the Great Pyramid, and these have been taken as confirmation of a buttress construction. However, these stones are not fully described as to their size, quality, angle, fineness of joint etc. The very absence of such information may itself solve the matter because a series of buttresses in cross section would display a pattern of face lines at about 75° to the horizontal, this being the critical plane of reference rather than the passage floor. The reports are not sufficiently complete to provide evidence that buttresses exist within this pyramid. There is another and more valid reason for these stones to exist, if laid on a horizontal bed and this would become clear if the process of raising stone up the side of the pyramid is considered in relation to the exposed core of Khafre's Pyramid. However, this is discussed fully in chapter 9.

In the last of the principal pyramids in my sequence, (Khafre's), the lines of the exposed core strongly evidence a coursed construction. The face work remaining near the apex shows the

Fig. 64 *The evolution of the stable core.*

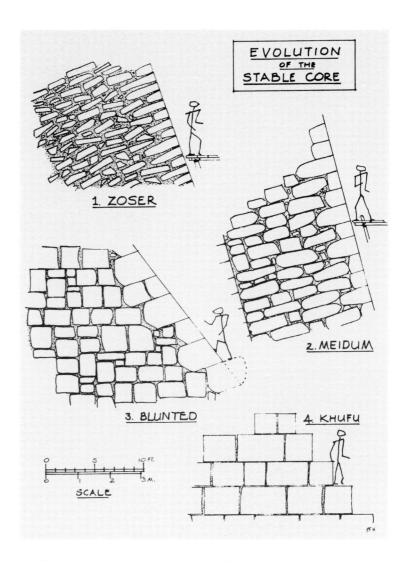

familiar pattern except that some of the stretchers are made up of two thinner stones laid one on top of the other to make up the course thickness.

This evolution which I have described opened with the 'buttress pyramid' where the face work was essential to its stability and reached maturity with the 'coursed pyramid', where its stability depended entirely upon the core (see fig. 64). These are essential differences which clearly divide the pyramids into separate groups both structurally, (in their anatomy), and mechanically, (in the method of their assembly).

7 Building stepped or buttress pyramids

With a clear understanding of the differences which separated the two kinds of structure previously labelled commonly as 'pyramids', it is easier to connect each type with its own building process. Putting the problem into simple terms it can be seen that raising buttress pyramids was a matter of building one sided masonry walls, while coursed pyramids required the laying of squared blocks in level courses. The two operations are quite unlike one another and this chapter examines the way in which the Ancient Egyptians – or anyone else with the same resources – would have tackled the first of the two types.

Generally speaking, the buttress pyramids consisted of about seven concentric layers with the exposed faces not exceeding thirty feet high and built of stones weighing from half a ton to one-and-a-half tons, according to the stage in the development. It is this scale of operations with which we have to come to terms (see fig. 65).

The first step would have been the setting out of the centre square and concentric buttress lines on to a previously levelled area of ground, ready to receive the type of structure shown in my simplified drawing (see fig. 66). Next, the centre core would have been raised to about chest height, followed by the start of the first buttress which would act as a stepping stone to allow the centre to continue. This process would have progressed until each section

Fig. 65 *Zoser's Step Pyramid at Saqqara. This was the first attempt to build a monument of this volume or height. The structure started as a much smaller pyramid and was later increased to the size we see now, 230ft high and nearly 400ft along one side of the base. A further buttress is hidden by the bank of sand.*

Fig. 66 *The buttress pyramid. A perspective section to demonstrate the principles: the top of each buttress would be capped with hard limestone laid to a slight fall; the dotted lines indicate the concentric pattern to be marked out on the ground.*

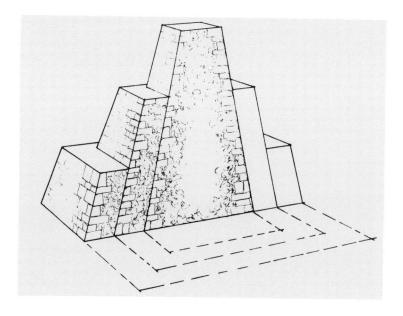

Fig. 67 *Raising a buttress pyramid. Shown here are the first two stages of raising a buttress or step pyramid. Building steps are brought up simultaneously at the centre of at least two sides. The face work is built from a wood scaffold which is dismantled as each step is finished. The un-faced parts of the buttresses can be reached from the buttress below.*

stood about chest height above the one below it (see figs 67 and 68).

This was almost certainly the sequence of work because every builder wants to gain as much height as possible before he has to add something temporary to his structure, such as a scaffold or a ramp. The buttress pyramid lends itself to making the best use of its own structure at the start of the building, and any other order of construction would involve the builders in raising free-standing faces even higher than the 30 foot faces left between the tops of successive buttresses.

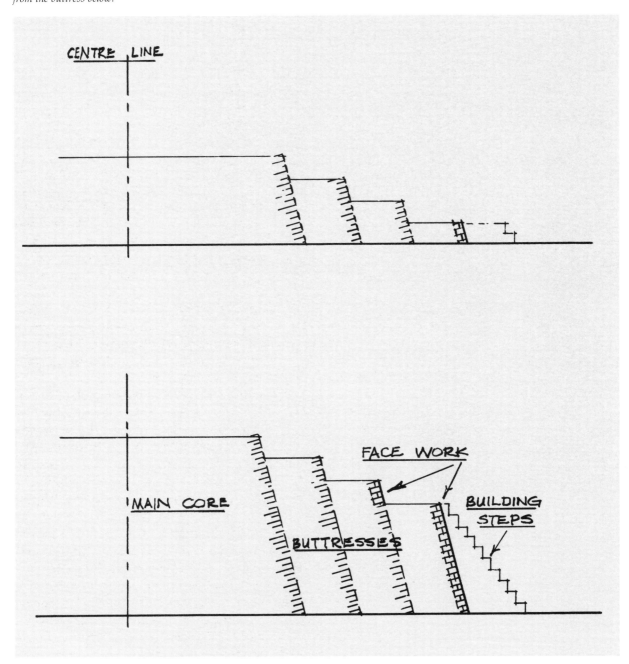

CENTRE LINE

MAIN CORE

FACE WORK

BUILDING STEPS

BUTTRESSES

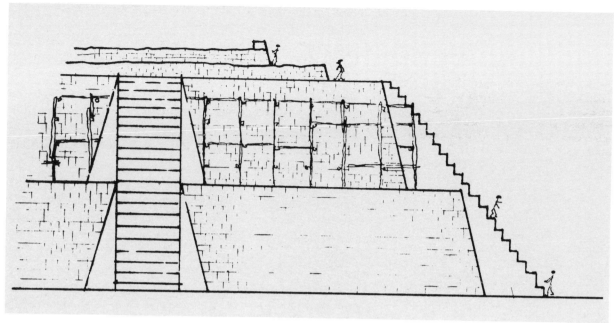

Fig. 68 *Front view of the third stage of the buttress pyramid after the two lower buttresses have reached full height. The scaffold has been removed from the outer buttress and is shown still in position on the next. One set of building steps is shown on the front with another set against the side. The two highest buttresses have been raised about 5ft without the need for a scaffold.*

The Ancient Egyptians have proved their competence as builders on the evidence of the work which has remained standing and we are entitled to infer that in doing this they developed the most efficient method for each particular job; in other words, there is a 'best method' rule which may be applied when considering possible alternatives in their building process, as long as the building methods are commensurate with the known contemporary skills and attitudes.

The nearest thing yet discovered to a buttress pyramid in the course of construction is one excavated by Goneim at Saqqara.[1] He has identified this as having been built by King Sekhemkhet who reigned for a short time early in the Third Dynasty, so that the pyramid comes after Zoser and before Meidum and could be said to occupy the position of number one-and-a-half in my sequence of six principal pyramids. Goneim established that the pyramid had never been finished, that the stump had probably been used as a quarry in ancient times, and that the centre now stands some 24 feet high with the adjacent buttresses at successively lower levels. The entire base is still evident below the present sand level, and measures about 380 feet square. Regretfully, Goneim could not complete a full report and we are not told whether the base stones of the outer buttress were laid as face stones, for dressing later. His photographs show that the masonry of the centre core and adjoining buttresses was made up of brittle, coarse stone laid in such thick mortar joints that the work could never have been intended for later dressing. This follows normal practice as the dressing was restricted to the outer exposed faces of the pyramid. His statement that the buttresses were built in two layers must be suspect because he says that this matches the work in other contemporary step pyramids, but an examination of Zoser's and Meidum does not confirm this. The buttress construction consists in both cases of a core with face stones bonded in, as shown in my sectional diagram (see fig. 64, chapter 6).

To return to my pyramid under construction (see fig. 68); my diagram shows that each buttress is now so high above its neighbour that the stones could no longer be 'heaved up' from one step to another, and that the 75° buttress face provided no foothold. Goneim reported that he had found ramps built up against the sides of the Unfinished Pyramid structure and that these totally enclosed all the faces. Unfortunately no details are given as to gradients and dimensions and his photographs do not make clear the disposition of the ramps, but this has not prevented other authorities from using these ramps, no more than 30 feet high, as sufficient evidence that all pyramids, even those over 450 feet high, must have been built with the aid of such ramps.[2] It is not reasonable to believe that the builders who raised the buttress pyramids some 200 feet high would have enclosed and hidden the entire structure within a vast mound of mud and stone chips. It is more likely that the access ramps were constructed to the lower levels but were no wider than was necessary for their use; the exposed parts of the face, particularly the angles, being reached from a temporary wooden scaffold, but only for assisting with the placing of the stones and for the later dressing.

As the structure grew the builders would have economised by forming much steeper ramps of bonded masonry and operated them as 'short' ramps using a rope method similar to the one suggested in my diagram (see fig. 16, p. 15). These ramps at higher levels could have been built at right angles to the buttress face, in short ramps going from one buttress top to another. This method has been suggested by other authorities, but never in conjunction with an operating method which could have worked in practice. The fact that the builders had by then devised some efficient lifting device (or mechanical advantage) is proved by the very weight of the stones in common use. A one-and-a-half ton stone, laid so precisely as those at Meidum, required exact and controlled handling – heaving about on some sort of sledge was not enough.

It could well be the case that experience in the building of Meidum convinced the masons of the economies to be gained by the innovation of an autostatic structure. These included better stability, larger stones and therefore less joints to weather, easier and safer handling and, most important of all, elimination of waste in resources caused by the construction of temporary ramps and scaffolding. It was a stroke of genius (a combination of master craftsmanship and intelligent thinking) to have devised a method of building construction that was so entirely self-contained. The innovation was almost certainly introduced when Meidum was cased with an outer mantle, before appearing again at the 'Blunted Pyramid' at Dahsur and all the later and most magnificent pyramids.

As an alternative to ramps, 'building steps' similar to my diagrams (see figs 69 and 70) could have been raised , whereby

Fig. 69 *A perspective diagram showing how the building steps could have been raised as the buttress pyramid grew higher. In practice the size of each step would have been smaller, but how much easier to climb steps than to struggle up a steep slope.*

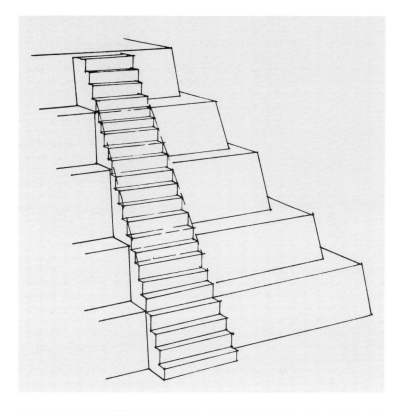

Fig. 70 *The completed buttress pyramid. The flat tops of the buttresses would be finished with a smooth sloping top as the steps and temporary scaffolding were removed. The line of the building steps shows how the Egyptians could have seen the possibility of continuing the steps round the whole structure until the shape of a pyramid resulted.*

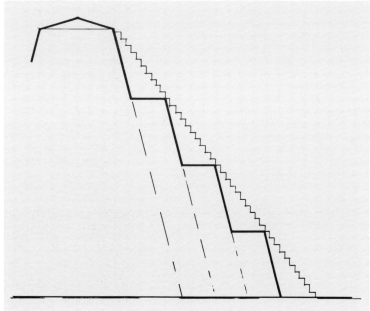

the stones could have been levered up from step to step, always under control, while the smaller material went in baskets or 'cradles'. This provides a need for the 'rocking cradles' which were discussed in chapter 2. This proposal fits in best with the workmanlike thoughts and practices which were so evident at that time. If such steps had been built at right angles to the face, the practice might well have given rise to the idea that the whole structure could be enclosed to give a smooth outer shape; this is precisely what was done at Meidum.

When the summit had been reached it was then necessary to cap the centre and the buttress tops with the best quality limestone laid with a 'fall' across the top surfaces, that is to say, with a gradient just sufficient to give a graceful finish and discharge any standing water. The arrises at the edges of these tops were given a distinct bevel but the main outer angles of the structure, running nearly vertically, were finished with a single, clean angle line.

It was the custom of these builders to lay their face stones with the sides, bed and top neatly jointed, but with the face itself left in the rough, sometimes with a definite knob to facilitate handling with levers when the stone was finally bedded.[3] Therefore the last stage of the work would have been to dress each face of the structure into a smooth plane surface with all the joints neatly pointed. This could only have been done to the superlative standards we can still admire if the whole of each face had been free at one time so that a geometrical check could have been made. The masons were, in fact, undertaking on a large scale the same process which has been described earlier in chapter 4, and for this to succeed all the edges around the plane had to be trued first. This rules out the suggestion that the entire structure was enclosed within a ramp and points to the more likely routine that any ramps were removed after the summit had been reached, and that the structure was dressed, face by face, starting from the top and working from temporary wooden scaffolds.

The scaffolds which we see in use today are elaborate latticeworks of steel tubing, but in those ancient times a few wood poles lashed together would have sufficed, the odd plank being put down only where the men had to work. There was no call for ladders as the men would have climbed wherever they needed to go.

There is no evidence to support the commonly held idea that the builders at this time were trying to build true pyramids. Conversely, the evidence more clearly points away from such a theory because it would have been so easy for them to have produced something much closer to, if not actually, the true pyramid form, whilst still using the buttress construction. The tops of the buttresses could have been finished off with stonework laid at a much steeper angle, so that the steps, which gave these early pyramids their striking outline, would have been much smaller; the illusion could have been extended if the summit had been taken up to a more pronounced point. When considering these early structures we must disregard the true pyramid shape, which had yet to appear on the Egyptian skyline, and accept that the builders were doing no more than building walls, as their experience had taught them, but leaning them together so as to stabilise a mound.

The Great Pyramid

8 Building the Great Pyramid

It is now possible to describe the sequence which was almost certainly the one followed by the Egyptians when they built the Great Pyramid. The present appearance of the pyramid with the core stones exposed clearly suggests that it was constructed as a coursed pyramid and would therefore have been a natural progression, following on after the Low Pyramid at Dahshur.

The final casing or dressing of the pyramid is a complex subject and will be dealt with in a later chapter; in the meantime, I propose to assume that all the stones are of the same quality and that the first operation is to construct a true pyramid. This will not alter the principles involved in the building process and will not affect the critical factor already established, namely that the structure must have been raised with stepped sides suitable for the jacking up system of raising the building stones (not to be confused with the buttress-type construction of pyramids).

The pyramid can be seen to have about two hundred level courses of squared stones, but there are several courses of different thicknesses, possibly arranged to accommodate a proportion of stones coming from thinner strata in the quarries (see figs 71 and 72). In order to appreciate the builders' problems it is

Fig. 71 *The core of the Great Pyramid was raised in level courses, the thickness of each course probably being governed by the sizes available from the quarries at any particular time. The base course is about 5ft thick and above the fourth course the average thickness is 2–3ft.*

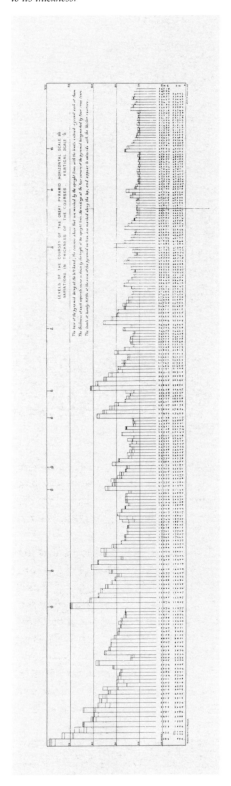

Fig. 72 Petrie has shown each course thickness to scale vertically, and emphasised the variation by extending the course horizontally, in proportion to its thickness.

essential to understand the various definite and vital properties of the solid pyramid form, the basic one being that the apex is positioned exactly over the centre of the base. Furthermore, if the base is horizontal then every horizontal section, or slice, taken through the pyramid will be an exact square which will sit 'true' over the base. The side of each slice will be parallel with the side of the base.

This horizontal slice is an essential part of the geometry because in practice it becomes each successive working platform as the building progresses. The masons would have been aware of these properties from their work of cutting and shaping stones on the benches (or 'bankers') and it was from this geometrical knowledge, acquired on a man-sized scale, that they were able to expand and form shapes to a super-human scale without loss of accuracy.

One of the arts of building is to assemble together manageable pieces of a material so that they will form a very much larger shape while still maintaining the original strength and texture of the material. The Egyptians took a manageable block of around two-and-a-half tons weight and put about two million of these together to form a stone pyramid, which was finished as neatly and accurately as though it had been cut in a single piece from a mountain of limestone.

Our builders do this today, using perhaps a quarter of a million small bricks to form the shapes of large buildings by laying one course accurately upon a preceding one. For the Great Pyramid the Egyptians used a 'brick' nearly a thousand times larger than ours, but they still understood the need to lay each one in its exact place to avoid the beginnings of an error which would increase as later courses were laid, distorting the shape of the structure. In fact, the greater the scale of the structure the greater the need to maintain accuracy in detail, starting from the lowest course of stones. An experienced mason would have known that to have piled the stones upwards in a haphazard manner, hoping to achieve a pyramid, would have resulted in an uneven shape that could never afterwards have been corrected.

Once the Egyptians had recognised the need to raise the pyramid in level courses, accurately laid, they were then faced with the problem of reducing the size of each successive course by just the right amount to produce the predetermined slope at the sides (see fig. 73). It is easy to assess the angle of a slope once it has been formed, but it is quite another matter to build up a slope piece by piece from nothing. This can only have been done by following one of the basic methods still used in building today, namely, by raising the corners, or angles, of the structure first and then filling in the straight parts between the angles. The same practice is followed by plasterers, who fix temporary wooden 'rules' up the angles at each end of a wall face and then work the plaster

Fig. 73 *The solidity of the masonry accentuates the frailty of the human body. The Ancient Egyptians who set these stones into position were probably of no greater stature than these youngsters. The foreground plinth stone would have weighed 10 tons before the angle was cut back to form the splayed face.*

between these edges. It is almost impossible to form a straight wall or a flat surface by starting from the middle and working outwards. In the case of a pyramid the angles are formed by the hip lines which are the guiding boundaries to the surface of each sloping side.

In the construction of any building there are three elements which combine together to make an accurate structure. These are a matter of solid geometry rather than design or structural detail and they can be listed in order of priority as, firstly, the 'primary blocks', which form the boundaries of each face, secondly, the 'facing blocks' and lastly, the core (or filling), which is hidden from view. The blocks which lie around the edges of any openings which penetrate the face can be termed as 'secondary' guide blocks. The terms 'primary' and 'secondary' are not in common use: I have introduced them myself to help emphasise the essential elements in the building process.

If you should wish to construct any building in bricks or blocks it will soon become clear that the primary guide blocks must be laid before any of the others. In practice, a bricklayer or mason will first 'raise his corners' for about three feet in height before he strings a line across to guide the setting of the facing bricks, or blocks, which lie between these corners.

The Great Pyramid contains no more than about 800 primary guides, which are the blocks forming the hips, one at each corner of 200 courses, and about 100,000 facing blocks; the remaining 2,100,000 blocks are all filling.

It was the correct setting of the 800 primary guides which determined the accuracy of the final shape. There can be no other shape which contains such a low proportion of primary guides in its make-up. The higher this proportion is for any structure, then the more complex it will be to construct, and the greater will be the cost.

Traditionally, certain trades have always been paid for their work on a piece-work rather than an hourly basis. This has the sound advantage that the customer pays only for what has been done and the tradesman can increase his earnings by extra skill or endeavour. Brickwork is one of these trades. Bricklayers keep in mind a basic price for laying one thousand bricks, and for this price they will mix the mortar, erect the scaffold, hump the bricks, and do all ancillary work such as fixing lintols* and frames. They can easily calculate from a drawing the number of bricks in any building, but before agreeing a price, they must gauge, by experience, whether there are any factors which will make these particular bricks more difficult to lay than the standard average. One of the things they have to judge is whether there is an unusual number of corners or breaks or openings because it is these elements, and not the straight runs, which take up the time. So in reality, they are assessing the proportion of primary and secondary guides: the principles which affect the cost of their work were just as important to the builders of the ancient pyramids.

There exists one extreme example, namely, where a circular wall is to be built when all the blocks of both the inner and outer faces must be classed as primary guides because none of the blocks can be set in a straight line between two corners but must be set individually against a template.

The pyramid builders therefore must first have laid the corner blocks of each course, and checked that these were correct before filling in the rest of the course, and then proceeding with the one above. The first course needed only to be laid down according to the setting-out lines described earlier and the builders probably left out a large part of each side so that the course blocks did not have to be jacked up and over the edge stones. When all the course blocks were in place and the last of the perimeter stones set, it was essential to check with boning rods that the top of the course was entirely level; although the stones may have been cut to an equal thickness in the quarry they could still have developed some unevenness in the process of laying. A bricklayer

* Ed: Peter Hodges used the alternative way of spelling 'lintol', offered for example by the *Concise Building Encyclopaedia*, compiled by T. Corkhill, Pitman Publishing. 'Lintol' is preferred to 'lintel' by many builders and some architects.

checks that the top of a new course is level before he lays the next one, so as to avoid passing on an error which will tend to increase higher up. The most difficult part of the work came with the setting of the corner stones for the next course, because these had to be 'set-in' from the edge in both directions and by just the right amount to start the hip lines running up to meet at the apex.

The builders needed to know the gradient of either the slopes or the hips; this must have been decided upon before the work had begun and then been recorded by establishing metal or timber framed 'masters' from which 'plumbing frames' were constructed. The suggestion has already been made, both by the author (in chapter 1) and by others, that the angle of the pitch may not have had any mystical significance but merely represented the steepest angle to which the builders could work. The controlling factor was most probably the need to jack the stones up the sides of the pyramid; the steeper the slope, the narrower the steps.

The only method for setting the corner stones in practice was to use a plumbing frame with a hypotenuse as long as practicable, but which would cover at least three steps or about ten feet. I have shown the method of using the frames (see fig. 39, p. 37), and any practical man can confirm that this is a very much more accurate process that it might appear at first to the layman.

There were other physical checks of the shape available to the builders, but before describing these it is necessary to realise that a pyramid possesses another important property, which is that the hips rise in the same vertical plane as the centre axis; expressed in practical terms it means that if you stand opposite the hip and look towards the pyramid then the hip line will appear to be vertical (as seen in fig. 5, p. 7). The north-west hip of the Great Pyramid faces over a cliff, but this would not have prevented a sighting from the lower ground looking upwards. For the builders of the pyramid it meant that if all four hips were seen to rise vertically and they were laid at the same angle to the horizontal, then they must have met at the apex point; in the event of an error some minor adjustment could have been made after the apex was reached, but it would have been a difficult task best avoided by careful building in the first place.

However carefully each hip stone had been set with the plumbing frame, it would still have been a wise, if not vital, precaution to have sighted these hip-lines from outside the pyramid against a vertical marker. In this way it could be seen if the hips were 'growing' correctly. This could have been done by sighting past a long plumb-line suspended from a scaffold erected outside the pyramid and set exactly over an extended diagonal from the base. Alternatively, a stone column or short wall could have been built, which would have stood during the twenty years that the work took to complete (see fig. 74). This suggestion may seem at first rather elaborate but the Egyptians were accurate builders and

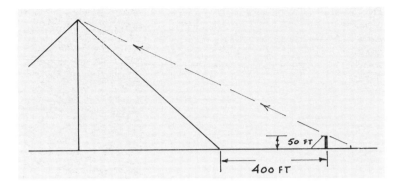

Fig. 74 *A view of the Great Pyramid with a temporary column 50ft high erected as a sighting marker to check the verticality of the hip line.*

well understood these basic geometrical properties and the use of the line of sight, and what is more, the evidence of the finished structures is there as proof of their competence. If the Great Pyramid were to be put up today with the aid of modern survey instruments, the same check would be made by sighting towards it with a theodolite, which is nothing more than a telescope which can be rotated up and down in a true vertical plane.

As an aid to understanding the three-dimensional problems, I made myself a kind of 'pyramid game' to test physically the process of building the pyramid corners accurately. I cut six pieces of chipboard about three-quarters of an inch thick, triangular in shape and in decreasing sizes, from about nine inches down to three. Each piece was cut so that it had one exact right-angle, but the hypotenuse of each piece was sawn at random.

Starting with the largest piece, I began to build up the corner shape and soon discovered that it was instinctive to follow a particular sequence. I used a bevel, or a master angle, to see that the steps were developing at the right pitch and then I checked that the steps were of equal width. After this I looked at the figure from above to make sure that the edges of the steps were parallel. I then assumed the figure must be correct, until I looked at it from table height to see if the hip line was developing in the vertical plane, and invariably it proved necessary to make some further fine adjustment.

Experiments with this model (see fig. 75) disclosed the difference between making drawings on a flat piece of paper and building up a solid form in three dimensions. The model showed how easily an error can begin and then aggregate as each successive course is laid, but at the same time it established that if the solid form satisfied all the visual checks that I have described then it must have adhered to the correct shape. The condition is absolute and leaves no room for any undisclosed error.

The model also established the need to build the pyramid working from the pitches of the side slopes, leaving the gradient of the hips to develop as a consequence. It is not possible in practice to start with a given hip gradient and set the corner stones from this information alone.

Fig. 75 *This model is assembled from loose pieces of chipboard. The process demonstrates that if the pieces are laid down so that the steps are equal and parallel, the gradient correct, and the hip line straight, then the solid shape must be growing correctly.*

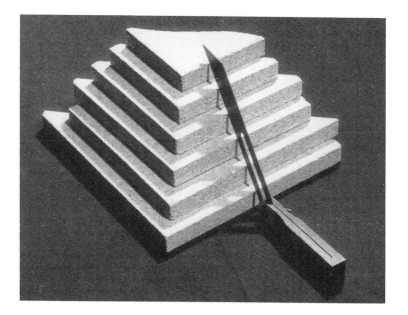

I recommend anyone to try the experiment, because the move from the flat plane to the solid form is immediately instructive and rewarding.

The sequence so far was therefore as follows: the Egyptians would first have checked the pitch of the slope using a plumbing frame, and then checked whether the step edges were parallel; this could have been done by standing on the working platform and sighting the edge of the new step against the ones below. At the same time the verticality of the hip line could have been checked from outside the pyramid.

The next of the essential properties to consider is the fact that each horizontal section, or slice, will be a level square. All building courses are best laid horizontally, and the checking of the general level of the courses could have been done by carrying water up to the working platform and forming a canal to repeat the process described earlier for setting out the base. Time could have been saved by measuring the height of a new course from the one below, but an error would soon have started to aggregate if the levelling were not checked after every few courses had been laid.

Having ensured that each course was level, the Egyptians had then to make certain that each one was square and lay truly over the base. The correctness of the square was simple to check by measuring the diagonal distances between the hip stones which were set up first at the corners of each course. Both the length of the sides and the right angles could have been measured by the same methods suggested for the base. (It was also important that no 'twist' in the shape was beginning to develop – see chapter 4. Such a twist would also have shown as a bend in the hip line). This type of solid structure would have needed constant and careful checking from each available point to detect the start of any basic errors. Even today, when surveying instruments are used to check levels and verticals, a competent foreman or builder will stand back from the work sighting one vertical edge against another and following the horizontal courses round from one elevation to another. The bricklayer or mason stands so close to his work that he cannot himself see the general form as it develops.

The craftsman in the building trade develops a greater instinctive knowledge of solid geometry than we realise, until a practical problem puts this knowledge to test. There stands on a certain site in the south of England a block of two semi-detached bungalows which are eleven inches wider at one end than the other, and yet the ridge and the eaves are all level and the tiled slope appears to be perfect. The error had started when the bricklayers mistook the marks on the profile board and at one end put the outside face of the wall where the inside should have been. Unfortunately the mistake was not spotted until the carpenters measured the brick shell to prepare the roof timbers. Equal rafters would have produced a falling ridge-board which would have shown up against the other level ridges on the estate. This would have been the greater evil and led to early detection, so, consequently, the rafters were cut individually in increasing lengths, and this kept the ridge height constant despite the widening span. The resulting roof slopes would no longer be rectangular and the top courses of tiling would have struck the ridge tile line at a tapering angle, there being five more courses at one end than the other, also inviting disaster; but this was hidden by distributing the taper evenly between all the forty courses up the roof slope. The men who rapidly worked out, in their heads, the solution to this crisis could well have faced the problems posed by building a pyramid if the task had been given to them.

Several Egyptologists have recognised the difficulty of raising the four hip lines with sufficient accuracy to meet at the apex but they have failed to appreciate the skill which builders acquire in bringing up a corner, or a wall face, block by block against a plumb rule. It is a skill learnt only by long practice and cannot be explained scientifically any more than the skill of a darts player or an archer. It has been suggested that an aiming point was necessary and that this may have been provided by the erection of a centre pole balanced on top of a tower (see fig. 76). Mendelssohn assures us that this was the case,[1] proved by someone discovering, in 1899, what was thought to be a post hole socket in the top of the pyramid at Meidum. This proposition may appear attractive to a layman but there are some details that need a closer look; how, for example, was the pyramid built in the first place in order to support the pole? How could a central high-level aiming point have helped in keeping the sides square? In fact the whole idea is

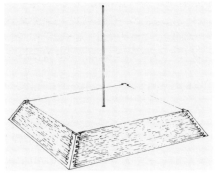

Fig. 76 *The problem of building a pyramid is to bring the four hips up so that they will meet at one common apex point. Authorities have suggested that a pole was first erected in the centre to be used as a guide during the building, but they cannot have considered the practical difficulties in finding such a pole or keeping it upright. The sketch shows the Great Pyramid with half its volume laid, when the pole would still need to be another 370ft high – the distance that the top of the cross on St Paul's Cathedral stands above the ground!*

unsound because a builder could not work in this manner; if he raised any sort of guides at all they would need to be at the hips, like the poles of a wigwam. Earlier writers may have had difficulty in re-creating the building process because they thought 'How could we have built the Pyramids?' instead of first posing the question 'How could stonemasons with their particular skills have done this?' and then followed with a careful study of those skills.

Progress on the site would not have been so simple as my description may have implied because the pyramid was not solid but had essentially to incorporate the funeral chambers and connecting passages. These enclosures had to be designed in detail and constructed integrally with the rising core which provided a working platform and a haulage access for the special stones. Those stones which lined the enclosures would have been finely shaped around the sides but laid with the face left in a roughly hewn state, to be dressed later from temporary internal scaffolds.

The detailed dimensions and gradients of the various enclosures have been surveyed and carefully described in many text books, so that my own contribution is merely to emphasise two points; firstly that such enclosures had to be formed integrally with the core and, secondly, that there had to be a sound method by which the heaviest stones could have been raised. This I have suggested in chapter 3 (see fig. 33, p. 30), with particular reference there to the roof beams of the main chamber, although it will emerge in later chapters that the pyramid must have required several thousands of stones, for facings, which weighed nearly double the generally accepted average of two-and-a-half tons each. If for some reason it was not convenient to provide an 'inside' set of steps for the heavy stones, then the same assistance could have been provided by raising a temporary set of building steps up against the outside of the pyramid, each step having a wide tread and a low riser.

There will be a further mention of the more detailed problems of stone handling, in chapter 9.

We can now visualise the whole scene at the pyramid site with thousands of men constantly in motion – on the ground moving the stones towards the base of the structure, in groups trimming or preparing various materials on the pyramid itself, and a constant upward movement as the gangs of hauliers jacked the stones up the stepped sides to the working level. In the midst of all this activity the master-builders and their assistants would be measuring and checking each movement of growth, some at the working levels and others from positions outside the pyramid looking inwards towards the work.

Herodotus quotes a period of twenty years for the completion of the Great Pyramid. Most authorities give cautious respect to this figure,[2] and I have taken it as a target in laying out my progress chart (table 4). No firm evidence has been offered to tie down this period but it seems reasonable to assume that the work could not have been done in less time, so that if my proportions are right then they will still form a valid basis if evidence comes to light to prove that the project occupied the more likely period of thirty years. The chart shows that the last three years have been reserved for the casing operation, which will be discussed fully in chapter 9.

If a period of seventeen years is to be taken as reasonable for the placing of the blocks, then it is essential to decide not only the consequent rate of 'block flow', but also whether enough men could have been fitted onto the sides of the growing pyramid in

Table 4

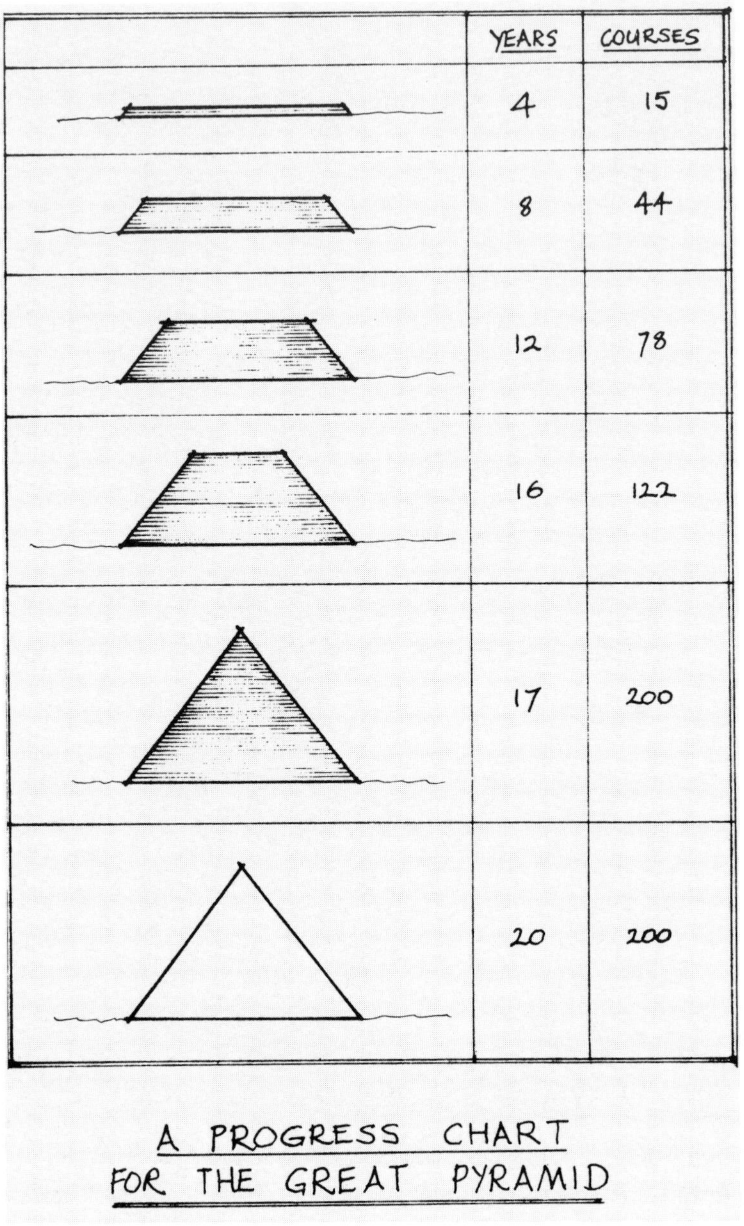

	YEARS	COURSES
	4	15
	8	44
	12	78
	16	122
	17	200
	20	200

A PROGRESS CHART
FOR THE GREAT PYRAMID

order to achieve such a flow. The lifting process must have been the critical factor, more than the transport or the handling at the working levels, in maintaining steady progress.

A simple way of equating the amount of lifting that had to be done against the capacity of the workmen is all that is required, and the invention of two special units of measurement will help in the calculation. These can be, firstly, the 'step' on the side of the pyramid, which suits the size of the stones being handled; and, secondly, the 'jack', being the vertical gain achieved with each push of the levers. It would be of no help to put these terms into linear dimensions. Assuming therefore that nine jacks make up one step and 200 steps make the height up to the apex, we have the basis of a motion study that can be related to units of time.

The simple sums which will follow can, of course, be done as a theoretical exercise, half a world away from the pyramids themselves, but undoubtedly the best place to do them is sitting at a table by the swimming pool of the Mena Garden Hotel, below the Great Pyramid and almost immediately on the prolongation of its northern axis. From here one can study in comfort the masonry of the northern face, noting the level courses and judging the size of the stones against the human figures working their way up the left-hand hip in their forbidden climb to the summit. It is these small bodies, climbing, sitting or standing gesticulating on the summit platform which help the keen observer to imagine the original builders at work and to believe that these vast structures were in fact raised by man alone.

I judge that the halfway block, numerically speaking, must lie about 48 courses (or steps) up from the bottom, so that the total number of steps made by all the blocks must be 2,300,000 x 48 or about 110 million in seventeen years. This time-scale reduces to about 6,000,000 per year and 18,500 per day (steps – not blocks). Now if there are nine jacks per step, then at five minutes for each step one experienced team would do 150 steps per day; at this rate 125 teams would have been needed at work together. This means that 125 teams working steadily for 350 days out of every year, for seventeen years, could have raised all the blocks into the Great Pyramid – provided that there was room for them to work. This can be checked at any level because the reduction in width as the pyramid grew was compensated by the extra height (see fig. 34, p. 31) but taking the bottom course and leaving half of one side to be reserved for handling larger stones, then a total length of three-and-a-half x 750ft = 2,625ft was available, enough to provide the 125 teams with the 21 feet that they each required. Of course, each team would have had its reserves, so that the block was kept moving constantly upwards while some of the men rested.*

This appears to contradict the popular theory that this work was done only during the period of the annual Nile inundation, but this has never been more than a theory, conceived by people

*Ed: a note by the author asks, "Can anyone still maintain that this rate of block flow could have been achieved by dragging the stones one behind the other up a long ramp?"

who had no firm idea as to how the work was done, and who had not picked up any clues that might have been offered. And plenty of clues there have been. Only this year* during my trips around the Giza pyramids my attention was called by hearing the buggy driver reciting what seemed to be the Penguin translation of Herodotus' description of the building of the pyramids, but he could never have read such a book; could it be that he had learnt it as by son from father and backwards through time to reach the guide who took Herodotus around the site about 450BC? A community which has no books will have been assiduous in passing down by word of mouth matters of importance or interest.

With the deduction that only a thousand men could have been accommodated on the pyramid sides and that this number was sufficient for the lifting work, then it is most probable that these men were made up of permanent gangs working throughout the year and that the annual 'temporaries' were put to work with the river transport, which could only operate during the inundation, and also to hauling the stones from the quarries to be stored around the base of the pyramid.

9 Casing the pyramids

The pyramid has been built and the summit reached, such an important event no doubt being celebrated with due reverence to the God in whose name the tomb has been raised. Nowadays we call this event a 'topping out' ceremony which is marked by a flag at the highest point and a round of drinks for the workers – paid for by the owner of the building and not the employer of the workmen.

Today's builder follows by starting work on the inside of the structure; the Ancient Egyptians had to work on the outside, converting the stepped sides into smooth, even surfaces with precisely straight lines at the intersections. The job had to be right first time, there was no chance of going back up to the top and starting again if the brilliant sunlight later revealed any irregularities.

To discover how this was done we must first establish the shape and size of the facing stones now missing from the Great Pyramid, because knowledge of this will help towards understanding the nature of the face work operation. These stones must have differed essentially in appearance from the blocks which can now be seen on the exposed edges of the core. The builders were traditionalists who improved their tried techniques and did not introduce novel methods into a large project so that the method of facing the Great Pyramid was one which fitted into a developing pattern.

The only examples of face work which remain as reference points in this development are those on pyramids at Meidum, Dahshur (The Bent) and Giza (Khafre's); from site observations and photographs I estimate the average stone weights to be, respectively, one-and-a- half, three and six tons. Table 3, (p. 54) discloses the rate of growth of this development and forms the basis for several references throughout this chapter.

The few facing stones which do remain in the Great Pyramid all lie in the five foot thick bottom course and cannot be representative of the stones which would have been used in the higher parts of the pyramid. A careful plan drawing of these few stones has been made by Clarke and Engelbach ('after Borchardt'[1]), but it would be misleading to attempt to use this drawing as any sort of clue.

The facing stones which remain at the other pyramid sites all display similar characteristics in their general shape, despite the fact that their sizes vary enormously; the length of the average stretcher normally equals about four times the thickness of the course, and they are always laid in level courses with a proper mixture of headers and stretchers. The proportion of length to thickness usually increases when the stones are used as quoins to bond the angles.

There still exists at the top of Khafre's Pyramid some of the original face work and, although the condition of the pyramid prevents any access to this cap, a great deal can be learnt from a careful study through binoculars. It can be seen that the facing stones are generally of the same thickness as the core stones behind them, but that occasionally two thin courses of facing have been laid so as to equal one course of the core. The core stones are all of compact proportions and present a different pattern in elevation to that of the face work.

The average thickness of each course in Khafre's Pyramid can be assumed to be about three feet and, bearing in mind the proportions of the length and width of the stones to this thickness, I have assessed the weights shown in my table 3 (p. 54). This table confirms that throughout this pyramid era there was a growing competence to handle and place larger stones and that at no time did the builders regress in this skill. The evidence of this progression is my basis for listing the facing stones on the Great Pyramid at about four tons.

The width of these largest stones on Khafre's Pyramid can be seen to be at least half as much again as the width of the building step, so that they could not have been safely balanced during the jacking process. My explanation as to how the builders overcame this problem offers two alternatives: the stones could have been jacked up on their edges, as their thickness for a 52° angle would be less than their width, or, preferably, a temporary filling could have been put onto alternate steps as the stone was raised. Such a filling, either of stone or a timber trestle, would have had the effect of doubling the step width while also doubling the jacking height.

It is clear that the builders have used the best quality stone available for the facework and that from this they have selected the very best stones for use in or near the hips. Hence these hips are the part of the pyramid which have most successfully withstood the weather, while the middle parts of the slopes are showing signs of erosion and structural failure. The strength in the hips has been further helped by the use of long stones, correctly bonded in the sound technique developed after Saqqara was finished but before the outer buttresses were added at Meidum. There can be no doubt that this technique would also have been used on the Great Pyramid and that its final appearance must have been much like the capping now remaining on Khafre's Pyramid.

The Egyptians were not the only early builders to demonstrate a theory that larger buildings needed larger stones despite the difficulties which this must have caused the masons. The Greeks in particular were adept in handling the larger blocks, and in the walls of the temple at Baalbek in the Lebanon I have been shown three stones of vast dimensions and claimed by the guide to weigh some 1,000 tons each. Unfortunately I was not then in a sufficiently critical frame of mind to take my own measurements and deduce the true weight but, nevertheless, the great authority Bannister Fletcher in *History of Architecture* quotes exact dimensions which must put the weight at about 700 tons each. Certainly, nothing I have seen in Egypt since has exceeded one-tenth of such a gargantuan monolith. The use of blocks as large as this can hardly be justified, but the Egyptians, with their more manageable facing stones, must still have been convinced that large facing areas called for large stones, either because they could imagine a greater strength from larger stones or because they had already learnt that erosion would begin at the joints, and thus the fewer of these the longer the work would endure.

Having discussed the nature of the outer stones, the next step in the search for a complete solution must be to decide how these could have been transformed into a smooth, steeply sloping surface. Any proposition put forward to suggest how these facing stones were fixed and shaped must satisfy a vital criterion, that the outer surfaces of the pyramid had been utilised as building steps both until the apex stone had been fixed and later as access for the masons who had to work on the final stage of the facing operation.

Herodotus, according to a translation given by Goneim in *The Buried Pyramid*, appears to sum it up quite neatly – "The highest parts of it, therefore, were finished first and afterwards they completed the parts next following; but last of all they finished the parts on the ground".* Unfortunately he does not say what he means, in masonry terms, by the word 'finishing', neither does he explain at what stage in the process the special facing stones were fixed; it is these two vital points which have to be settled by close reasoning.

Bearing in mind the essentials of the problem, it is not too difficult to see that the Egyptians had only two choices open: either to fill in the spaces between the steps, or to cut off the steps themselves so as to leave a smooth surface. These two operations I propose to describe as 'casing' or 'trimming' respectively.

The casing method, which is illustrated by a diagram (see fig. 77), assumes that the casing stones were fixed to the stepped core as a final operation after the apex had been reached. The fine limestone casing blocks would have been cut to shape on the ground, jacked up the pyramid and then bedded into position on the steps. The drawing shows that every course needed to be undercut below the course above, a difficult but not impossible job.

*Ed: other translations give the same information.

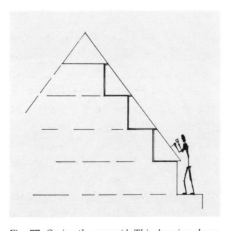

Fig. 77 *Casing the pyramid. This drawing shows the casing method of completing a pyramid. The mason is putting the finishing touches to the casing stone which has been bedded in course number 197 of the Great Pyramid.*

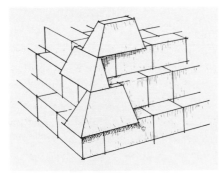

Fig. 78 *Perspective sketch to demonstrate how it would have been possible, using the casing method, to have set the prepared hip stones down the whole length of the hip before filling in the sides.*

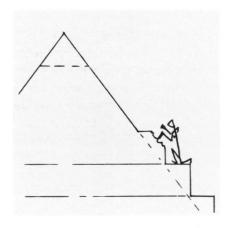

Fig. 79 *The trimming method, whereby each step would be cut off by hand, the steps being tackled successively from the apex stone downwards.*

The sequence would have been that the hip stones were first set down all four corners, from top to bottom (see fig. 78), and the lines of these could have been checked and adjusted, if necessary, before any further work was done. This arrangement would have been possible because the outward splay of the hip-line leaves a foothold for the masons below each hip stone. After this had been done, the casing stones along each step could have been set to a line sighted between each pair of hips.

However, the promises of theory do not always survive the realities of practice, and I consider that there are two weaknesses which would have deterred the Egyptians from any extensive use of the casing method. First, that the comparatively soft core stones would have become so badly worn during the long building process that each casing stone would have needed wedging up into position, and thus not be solidly bedded on the step; and, second, that the undercut joint would not have been an adequate seal against wind and weather.

Additionally, there are other relevant items of evidence which convince me that it was the 'trimming' method which the Egyptians most commonly employed (see fig. 79). This method involved the cutting away of the whole stepped surface after the apex stone had been fixed. Visitors to the pyramids who have judged for themselves the vast scales involved might say that such a task could never have been accomplished by hammer and chisel alone, but a careful study will show that this can have been the only solution.

The masons of the pyramid era had become accustomed to the practice of building stone walls in which the face of each stone was left in a roughly hewn state, to be trimmed and smoothed after the whole structure was finished and immediately prior to the removal of the scaffolding. This is the one operation which they did differently from masons today, who finish the face side before a stone is hoisted and set and then cover the work with a thick layer of slurry as a protection. Later, as each lift of a scaffold is removed, the masons clean off the slurry and make any final repairs to the pointing or the stone surfaces.

There are several examples of early Egyptian masonry to be seen which were evidently abandoned before the finishing stages of the project had been reached, one particular example being the tomb chamber of the ruined pyramid at Meidum. A further example is the base of the Third Pyramid at Giza, where the two bottom courses have been left with the stone surfaces roughly hewn back to the general slope of the sides. Some writers have taken this latter example as evidence that the whole pyramid must have been in this condition during some stage of its construction,[2] but it needs only a little thought to refute this theory, because with the sides in this condition there would have been no foothold for the masons. The bottom two courses may well have been trimmed from the ground, but anything much higher than this would have been out of reach.

The better quality casing stone would have been more durable than the core blocks, and thus more suitable to serve as building steps during the long period of construction; any step edges which became damaged would, in any event, be cut away during the final trimming stage. The trimming method had the further advantage that a steady supply of the casing stones would have been needed throughout a building process, thus spreading the work for the quarries and saving storage space on the site.

Trimming the Great Pyramid would have produced about 56,000 tons of mixed stone dust and chippings, a quantity which must appear vast to people of this decade whose constant objective is to reduce manual labour and eliminate wasteful use of materials. However, this quantity has to be considered in relation to the millions of tons of stone quarried and man-handled to create the whole structure, and on this basis it is less than one per cent of the whole. In proportion, it is no more that a skin three-quarters of an inch thick round the outside walls of an average modern house.

It is important to remember that this quantity of stone would in any case have had to be chiselled away at some stage during the building process, because the evidence we have been offered by archaeologists all points to the stones having been removed from the quarries in a rectangular shape rather than prised from the rock with one end already splayed. If the stone had been trimmed in the quarry before despatch, then there should be evidence of an unusual quantity of 'arisings' in or about the quarry, but if they were trimmed in situ then there should be 56,000 tons of foreign limestone chippings close to the cliffs of Giza. The builders of the Great Pyramid were the first on this particular scene, so that tipping must have been done over cliff edges or into the local quarries from which the core stones had been taken.

The discovery of such materials would help to confirm my theory, because if the trimming of the stones had been done before they were fixed then the place to have done this would have been in the quarry. The stones then would have been lighter to transport. *

If all the evidence points to the probability that the pyramid was trimmed after construction, this operation is so unusual to builders of this century that it is wise to study the problem from start to finish and try to deduce what difficulties the Egyptians would have faced and what sequence of operations they would have evolved in order to complete the work. They had the advantage of experience, a sophisticated competence in site organisation, and all the other skills and degrees of knowledge which have been discussed in earlier chapters, but it still could not have been easy to set the stones down so as to form the exact pyramid shape.

*Ed: chippings have been found at the base of the Great Pyramid, during the excavation of the Temple of Isis, by Michael and Angela Jones.[3]

While it may have been essential to bring up the pyramid sides in steps, the hips, which were the controlling lines of the growing shape, could have been dealt with by one of two methods. The masons could have cut each hip stone to its final shape as it was laid; or, alternatively, they could have left the hip stones in their rectangular state to be trimmed later with the rest of the pyramid.

In either event the top outer corners of the hip stones were available as marker points when checking the geometrical progression of the solid. The photograph (see fig. 80) shows how one hip of the pyramid would have appeared after six courses had been laid with the hips cut to shape. The hip stones are shown laid in alternate directions so that they bond into the adjoining casing stones, which themselves provide a foothold for the masons. It can be seen that the maximum sloping height at the hips, without a foothold, is only two courses, or approximately the height of a man. My drawing (see fig. 39, p. 37) shows men using a plumbing frame to set these hip stones to the right pitch, an operation which would be similar if rectangular stones were being used.

When they had reached the apex and verified that the four hips

Fig. 80 *This model shows how the bottom few courses of one hip would look if the hip stones were cut to shape as the pyramid rose. These courses are just over one inch thick (five courses rise 6in) so that the Great Pyramid to this scale would be about 20ft high and 30ft wide at the base.*

were straight and true from top to bottom, it only remained to cut back the building steps to a sloping face using the hip stones as a guide at both ends of each course. Needless to say, this had to be done one course at a time, starting from the top; if work had started all over the pyramid simultaneously it would have meant that each man was cutting away the support from under the men above. At this stage of the work there would have been a considerable bottle-neck in the progress, as only comparatively few men could have been employed around the upper courses at the commencement of the trimming operation; since all the stones had by then been fixed, there was nothing else which the masons could do on the pyramid itself.*

With the alternative method, the shaping of the hip stones would have been left to be done as part of the final trimming operation, and when the apex was reached the top of the pyramid would have looked like my photograph (see fig. 81). I have numbered the courses on the assumption that there was a total of 200, the top two being occupied by the apex stones. It would have been too difficult to cut this in situ, and it is more likely to have been fashioned out of several pieces of very hard stone, such as granite, taken to the top and re-assembled. Scholars have suggested that some of those stones may have been covered with gold, a plausible idea which would have given great emphasis to the apex in the brilliant Egyptian sun.[4]

The trimming process required that each step should be cut

*Ed: the work of finishing the interior, the valley temple and the mortuary temple was in hand – also the small exterior pyramids, and the boat pits.

Fig. 81 *A model to show how the top of the pyramid might have looked immediately after the apex stone was fixed. The Great Pyramid originally had about 200 courses and the scale of the model mason assumes that the top courses would not have been as thick as those lower down. This model assumes the 'trimming' method used for casing – see text.*

away separately, starting from the top, and as each sloping surface emerged it had to be smoothed to its final finish. I have mentioned earlier that any plane surface needs to be formed by obtaining true edges first and then working the plane surface between these edges. It was, therefore, essential to cut the hip-lines for the entire pyramid before trimming any of the steps. The line required lay inside the stone as a theoretical line joining the bottom of one hip stone to the bottom of the one below it, and it was necessary to cut away the corner of the step until the line was 'exposed'. The photograph shows how this could have been done (see figs 82 and 83), and I have drawn on the model the position of the emerging hip line. If this were first done down the whole length of the pyramid it would have been possible to make any slight adjustments and ensure that the hips would be straight and true before cutting away the steps.

This description may seem to the layman to be rather a lot of

Fig. 82 *The top, ready to trim.*

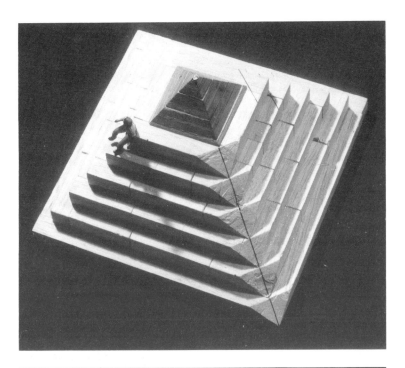

Fig. 83 *The final stage of the 'trimming' method would have been to trim the structure starting from the top and working downwards. The masons could have first exposed the four hip lines down the whole length of the pyramid by cutting off the corners of the steps as shown on the model.*

fuss about a simple matter, but I can assure the reader that this is the most difficult stage in the whole operation.

I did hold out a promise at the beginning of the book that anyone who persevered to the end would then be competent to direct the construction of a pyramid and should you have already raised one – full size or to a smaller scale – you will understand how critical these moves must be. After cutting away the upper steps there can be no going back to correct any irregularities which begin to appear; most likely these would take the form of a wobble in the hip line or gentle horizontal corrugations in the side faces. How the trimming process was mastered is the greatest mystery of the whole process.

The model shown in the photographs (see figs 80–83) does not show the lower 192 courses, and it requires a considerable effort of imagination to appreciate the wonderful head for heights which the masons must have cultivated. When standing on the top they were at a height equal to the cross on St Peter's Cathedral in Rome and looking down an unbroken flight of stairs much steeper than is found in any dwelling today. There were no guard rails or any other form of security available while they struggled to lift and slide the great stones into position. I believe that climbing the Great Pyramid today in order to sample this horrifying experience is prohibited,* and there can be few other physical locations in the world which could provide such a place in which to work, unsecured and unprotected.

Could this vast trimming operation have been accomplished within a reasonable time? It is not possible to be accurate in such an estimation, as we do not know exactly which tools the builders used, only that they had long experience in stone dressing and the use of good copper chisels and intensely hard pieces of abrasive stone.

If a mason could have reduced a step one yard long in five days working, then the task would have taken three years, provided that enough men were available to fill each step in turn, with 1,000 men being needed for the bottom step. Assuming that the figure of twenty years for the building time is correct, then it divides as seventeen years to reach the apex and three years to complete the trimming.

Although the stones were laid in level courses, it is not unusual to find instances where the upright joint between two stones in the same course is not vertical. These leaning joints must have caused a great deal of extra labour; the two adjoining stones would have had to be trimmed to fit up on the working platform instead of being cut square in the quarry before delivery. There seems to be no valid reason for this practice, unless the Egyptians thought that a splayed heading joint in some way strengthened the whole structure. It would have been possible to lay the facing stones after completion of the core and immediately before starting the trimming operation, but it is my belief that for the Great Pyramid they were bonded in around the edges as each course was laid.

The exposed core of the pyramid shows stones which must have been bonded into the missing layers; the irregular edges could not have been suitable as building steps (see fig. 84).

A recent publication,[5] includes numerous drawings purporting to show how the pyramids were built but, in reality, these drawings confuse rather than instruct; the author's suggestions are impracticable. There is one drawing in particular (see fig. 85) which shows the trimming operation being done from a three-tier scaffold with men working simultaneously on six successive rows of steps; if the men had worked like this they would have cut

*Ed: every year fatal accidents occur when someone stumbles, and is unable to regain a foothold before gravity takes charge.

Fig. 84 *The south face of the Great Pyramid at sunset when the horizontal light emphasises the irregular bonding at the edge of each course where the facing stones have been removed.*

Fig. 85 *Copy of a page from David Macaulay's book* Pyramid. *The scaffold is not really necessary, as my next drawing shows.*

the support from under the scaffold and from under one an-
others' feet; my sectional drawing (see fig. 86) discloses this
clearly. I mention this example because it shows the danger of a
superficial study not followed through by confirmation on models or by 'thinking through' a problem to its conclusion.

The photographs of Khafre's Pyramid (see figs 87 and 88)

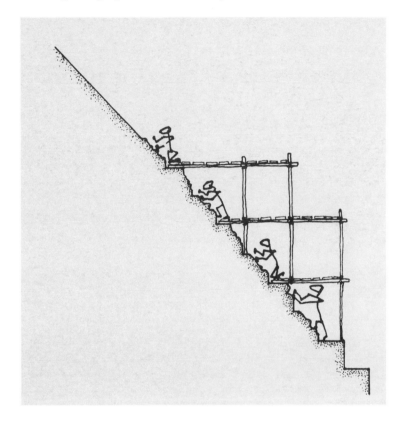

Fig. 86 *My sectional drawing of the proposal
shown in fig. 85: not only is the scaffold
unnecessary, but the men are undermining each
other and the scaffold support.*

disclose another feature which is relevant to any enquiry into the
probable building sequence. It can be clearly seen that the layer of
stones immediately behind the facings must have been of very
soft material with the result that they have eroded away during
the years of exposure since the casing was removed. This has
revealed an inner core of harder, well squared stones laid header
pattern and with their outer edges set in straight lines. These
headers were never bonded to the next outer layer. These course
edges would have been ideal to act as building steps and there
must be a strong inference that the strength to be obtained from
bonding was relinquished in favour of creating the steps, the
regular header pattern being quite different to the serrated edge
of the Great Pyramid core or the mainly stretcher work of Khafre's
final casing.

It is surprising that the existence of this unique pattern does not
appear to have been the subject of comment; it is reasonable to
suggest that the core had been completed at the stage before the
soft intermediate and the harder facing stones were added, prior

Fig. 87 *The Second Pyramid at Giza, built by Khafre. The upper part of the pyramid shows a portion of the original outer limestone facing stones. Below this can be seen traces of an irregular inner core with straight-edged steps. The lower part is covered by the disintegrating remains of the softer stones which had been placed immediately behind the facing stones.*

Fig. 88 *An enlarged view of the hard core of Khafre's Pyramid. It can be seen that the steps have straight edges with quite a different appearance from those on the core of the Great Pyramid.*

to trimming. The probable building sequence is shown in my drawings (see figs 89–94).

It would be difficult to argue that a ramp had been used for this process which, like adding another layer to a buttress pyramid, had to be done by starting all over again at ground level. It may be the case that the harder core stones which can now be seen are similar to those through which the smaller passage in the Great Pyramid is supposed to pass, but if they are then the theory that pyramids were built by adding accretion faces is finally demolished because they do not form part of an inclined buttress

Fig. 89 *The building of an eight-course pyramid The following diagrams represent a small pyramid being raised by the same sequence as that probably followed at Khafre's Second Pyramid. The first two courses are laid.*

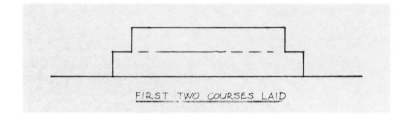

Fig. 90 *A third course is added.*

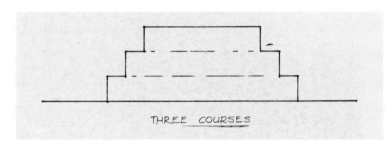

Fig. 91 *The core is finished, in regular building steps.*

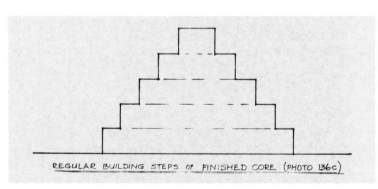

Fig. 92 *Two courses of intermediate and facing blocks have been added.*

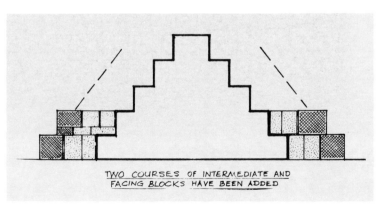

Fig. 93 *The top of the core is reached. The left hand side of the diagram shows how the thinner courses could have been brought out to avoid the small steps which appear on the right.*

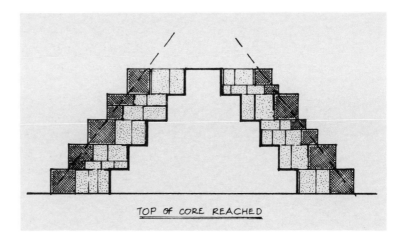

TOP OF CORE REACHED

Fig. 94 *Trimming the sides from the top downwards.*

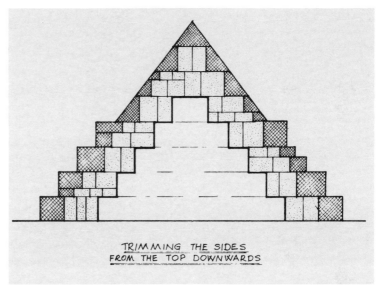

TRIMMING THE SIDES
FROM THE TOP DOWNWARDS

but are laid parallel to the final pitch of the pyramid face. The two outer courses therefore enclose, not accretion faces, but regular 'planes' of building steps the spacing of which may determine that the construction advanced in concentric stages rather than successively in completed courses. There seems no clue in sight which helps us to decide which was the method used; it is a matter for speculation.

10 Further aspects

There is one further operation which needs to be discussed if your understanding of pyramid building is to equal that of the Ancient Egyptians. I have established how the stones could have been lifted up into the pyramids but I have said nothing about the difficult task of lowering them gently into their final positions. Years of work by the Egyptians had developed the lifting process into one which would give the maximum possible vertical gain in the quickest possible manner; the lowering process needed to be one which provided a fine degree of control over the stone during the last few moments of its journey to become a permanent part of the structure.

The problem of how this was done without the use of any overhead lifting device is one which must not be left unresolved. It was the builders' most critical manoeuvre. The difficulty of the task and the magnitude of the achievements have been recognised,[1] but compared with some of the other problems, this operation seems to have received little detailed consideration. There are numerous drawings of stones on ramps, rollers or sledges, and even some showing the stones engirthed with ropes,[2] but none of these have shown the final moment when a stone was bedded down without leaving any marks of either tools or slings. Petrie said: "the setting of such large masses with such close joints at side and base is beyond our experience".[3]

It is necessary to look carefully at the process of laying down a block and to note which steps are essential to that process. When a bricklayer lays a brick he taps it down on to a soft mortar, and leaves it there. It is very rare for him to pick it up and start again unless he needs to chop it down to size, in which case he will first 'offer' it over the space to judge the length he requires, but he will not let the brick touch the mortar. This is merely a precaution to prevent mortar splashing about when he chops at the brick with his trowel.

It is quite a different operation for a mason to set down a large stone because the bed and sides have to fit exactly against their neighbours with only the thinnest grout between them. He must first offer the stone right into its place to check all the faces, raise it again, spread the grout, and then bed the stone finally into place. It is as well to use the correct terms; chickens lay eggs and bricklayers lay bricks but masons always 'bed' stones.

The joints in the earlier tombs such as Zoser's at Saqqara were quite thick and the mortar needed to be of a plastic or 'fatty' mix so that it would stay in place between the irregular surfaces of adjoining stones; a good consistency would have been that of a cow-pat. If a mix was too dry or 'sharp' then the stone would not bed down, because the mortar would not squeeze out or easily mould to the shape of the new stone; if it were too thin, like a grout, then it would run out of the wall. This matter of consistency was one of vital importance because it controlled both the bedding of the stone and the eventual stability of the wall; success depended on experience and judgement, each circumstance varying according to the thickness of the joint, the suction of the stone surface, the weights of the stones and even the temperature of the working day. The same factors affected, in just the same way, the bricklayers or masons who built our own houses – whether this happened five days or five hundred years ago.

The outer surfaces of Meidum (see fig. 95) show that the one-and-a-half ton facing stones were laid with a fine neat joint

Fig. 95 *The south-east angle at Meidum, where it emerges from the mound. Any three courses equal the height of a man, and the larger stones weigh one-and-a-half tons each. The stones were left roughly hewn because this part of the buttress was covered by an outer layer. The mortar which separated the outer layer can still be seen adhering to the face. This is an easterly view looking across the fertile Nile valley towards the Eastern desert. The Nile would have flooded annually right up the sand line which can be seen at the foot of the cliff.*

around all four edges; for such work to have been accomplished so accurately the builders must have contrived a competent working routine, on which they subsequently improved to the degree that their grandchildren were able to bed the four ton facing stones at Giza so closely that no Egyptologist or television commentator has since been able to force a knife blade between them.

A rough core stone could have been turned off the toes of the levers fairly easily because the core stones were not laid with close joints, but a facing stone had to be lowered gently and precisely into place. Let us consider in detail the bedding of a face stone weighing about four tons and being laid as a header up against the preceding stone in the same course. The levers would have been too thick to operate within the joint so that each stone had to leave the quarry with 'jacking knobs' left protruding at each end – or side, as required – enabling the levers to bite at a point above the bed level (see fig. 96). These knobs would have been 'bumped off' when they were no longer needed. The stone could have been rested on battens while it was offered for a fit, then the bed checked, cleaned and grouted, the battens removed and the stone lowered (see fig. 97). There is unfinished work which shows evidence that these jacking knobs were used.[4]

Fig. 96 *The levering method for dealing with a facing stone. There would be two levers at each end.*

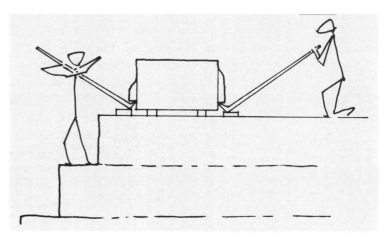

Fig. 97 *A facing stone lying on battens ready for lowering into position. The jacking knobs will be cut off later.*

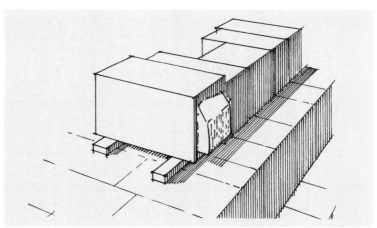

On the basis of this sequence it would have been simple to have laid a facing course around the entire edge of the structure but in fact the pyramid builders also laid another ring, of intermediate stones, immediately behind the facings; and in doing this they made for themselves a very difficult task. The small portion of the base course which remains at the edge of the Great Pyramid shows that these stones were laid almost as closely as the facings and immediately backing them, similar to my drawing (see fig. 94, p. 99). Borchardt has drawn these out in accurate detail,[5] but the essential elements of the pattern must have existed all round the pyramid and it is clear that the intermediate stones had only two adjoining faces free for jacking. The builders could have made their task so much easier if they had staggered these stones so that the joints fell mid-way between the facing joints but this was not the case and it is up to us to suggest how the work was done. Only one Egyptologist seems to have spotted the difficulty and speculated on a solution; this was J-P. Lauer who discussed the matter in some detail, eventually suggesting that the stone might have been slid sideways into its final position when the levers could no longer be accommodated.* His solution required that the stone should be lowered onto a mortar bed which had to act as a lubricant during the sliding process, but he accepted that the scheme might not have been feasible.

Lauer has given the chemical composition which he found in-situ but this does not really help us towards a solution because the builders had selected their mortars on the basis of physical behaviour rather than chemical content, of which they would have been ignorant. It was a matter of consistency and viscosity which decided if a grout was a suitable lubricant; just as a medieval builder added cow dung to certain mortars and my own craftsmen add milk or tallow to a lime wash, so the Egyptians may have added an organic material which is not now recognised as a particular building material.[7]

It is not difficult to establish that a four ton facing block would have needed a sideways thrust of about five tons to move it, laid dry, and about two to three tons if a lime-based grout were used and both stones had been well wetted to reduce suction. A great deal of water would have been used up throughout the operation, particularly as the grout had to retain its liquidity while one of the jacking knobs was bumped off.†

Could such a sideways thrust have been provided in practice? One man could exert a pressure of about one-sixth of a ton for a short time only, and with men pushing and some pulling with ropes along a timber beam, the proposition might just have worked. However, they would have found themselves in considerable difficulty if the stone had not bedded properly and had needed to be taken out for a second try; they could only have cut wedge slots in the top joint and turned it over backwards and out. There is a tomb painting made about a thousand years after the

*Ed: Peter Hodges did not complete notes for this reference but see [6].

†Ed: the author regarded the provision of water as a subject for further study – see end of his Appendix.

*Ed: reproduced in my chapter on
levers, fig. 113, p. 133.

pyramids were built,[8] which shows a large statue lashed onto a sledge for transportation; the lashings have been tightened by twisting with a wooden batten, in the form of a tourniquet.* This is another device for obtaining a mechanical advantage of a high ratio and the same principle might have been used to pull the stones into position by encircling previously laid areas of masonry, and the new stone, with about six ropes one above the other. The idea is pure speculation on my part based on the firm evidence that the builders, having no cranes or pulleys, had always developed simple devices to a more advanced degree than we today would consider to be worth the effort.

The only other alternative to sliding the stone would have been to leave extra material on one side of the stone so as to keep the centre of gravity away from the internal angle of the recess until the stone was bedded. The extra material could then be bumped off in-situ (see figs 98 and 99). There is plenty of scope for a better solution but this can only come from someone who has personally handled and mastered the obstinacy of a four ton block of stone.

The traveller who sees only the largest pyramids at Giza is most puzzled as to how a pastoral society could have worked out the organisation that could handle such millions of tons in dead weight of stone. The answer is that the builders of each pyramid have simply improved and enlarged the industry which already existed before they began their particular task. Starting from the time when King Zoser built an unusually large mastaba tomb, the organisation just grew and grew with each succeeding generation and with each new project, until reaching a zenith at Giza. There is not one of these major projects which could have been handled without the accumulation of previously gained experience.

The existence of this 'building momentum' is something which can be studied with a view to relating it to the time scale of the period. The momentum was like a flywheel constantly accelerating; it could not be stopped and later re-started like a clock but ever increased its speed until, inevitably, it burst, never to be reconstituted. The extent of the machine which drove this flywheel far outbalanced the pastoral activities of the community, and its products – the pyramids – dwarfed any other permanent results of man's effort at that time. Both the quality and the quantity of the work increased more and more rapidly during the two hundred years of the pyramid era considered in this book, committing ever larger and larger gangs of men – at the quarries, throughout the chain of transport and on the site with handling, lifting and laying of the blocks. Such a sustained torrent of effort could not have been suddenly stopped without a traumatic effect throughout the kingdom. The consequence to the general stability of the community would have been so serious that any new king must have felt compelled to keep the momentum going on his accession.

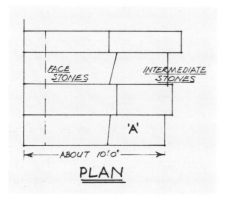

Fig. 98 *Diagram to show that the intermediate stones could not have been levered into position with only two adjoining faces accessible, if they had already been trimmed to size.*

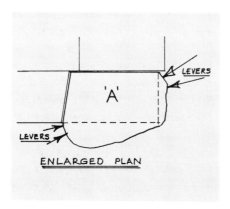

Fig. 99 *The stones must have been levered in with surplus material left on the free sides, and then trimmed in situ.*

*Ed: for a reasoned summary of political events at the end of the Fourth Dynasty, see *The Pyramids of Egypt*.[11]

†Ed: see my note, chapter 9, p. 89.

It may have been the case that the momentum came to an end naturally during the reign of King Khafre, after a time of political unrest[9] following the death of Khufu.* There is no sign of any decline in the quality of the work as proved by the third and smallest of the main Giza pyramids, built by Khafre's successor, Menkaure.[10]

I would like to suggest that some of my practical explanations have opened lines of enquiry which only archaeologists are competent to explore. If the use of levers on a large and sophisticated scale can be accepted, then there must exist evidence which has previously been ignored or passed unrecognised for its true worth. There is a case for re-examining any paintings, hieroglyphs and ritual foundation deposits of the Third Dynasty.

If the pyramids were 'trimmed' as the final stage of their construction, then the debris, or 'arisings' as they are called in the trade, must still lie close to each site.† It has been established that the outer casing stones were cut mainly from a first quality limestone which had been brought across the Nile from the eastern cliffs (the lower courses of Menkaure's pyramid are of granite; also "part at least of the lowest course" of Khafre's)[12] and consequently the arisings of this foreign material must have been deposited at Dahshur and Giza, and be capable of identification against the local stone.

An important facet of life during the Third and Fourth Dynasties must have been the attitude which the masons established towards their tasks and also towards the remainder of the community. It is an interesting speculation as to whether they regarded pyramid work as a special honour, so that membership of one of the teams conveyed a privilege which set its members in a class above others. Whether or not such work conferred a higher social status, we can be sure that the best workers and the best company would be found at the highest levels where the work was the hardest and the most dangerous. Danger was always present although the men were experienced, skilled and best able to balance themselves without the encumbrances of shoes and heavy protective clothing. From personal experience of various kinds of work, I would estimate that a project the size of the Great Pyramid would have seen at least 600 fatal casualties, three times the number to be expected if the men had been employed on normal building work but only a fraction of the casualties to be suffered if the men had spent the twenty years at war with their neighbours.

I have suggested earlier that the community may have resented having to support a large number of state workers, but this was pure speculation and historians may be ready to establish that the construction of a royal necropolis was regarded as being essential to the prosperity and safety of the kingdom. There may exist contemporary references which establish the peasants' attitudes to the continuing building activities. Considered in retrospect, these vast activities could be seen as an unwarranted excess which, like all abuses, grow and burn themselves out, weakening the community in the process.

My table 3 (p. 54) shows the sequence of development through six principal pyramids allied to the increasing size of the stones being handled by the builders, but it requires the skills of the archaeologist to determine more closely the starting dates of each structure.

The preceding chapters represent my endeavour to deduce and describe a valid method which could have been used to build the great stone pyramids. Essentially the test of my work is whether you, after reading these chapters, feel confident that similar pyramids could be built by this method today. There would be no need for spaceships, magnetic fields or giant-sized men; only human skill and ingenuity. My aim has been to reveal the true simplicity of the Egyptians' achievement.

Appendix

The building of a pyramid presents unique problems, most of which can only be mastered in one particular way. The Ancient Egyptians, without cranes or pulleys at their disposal, had no option but to use methods which we can deduce for ourselves, and it is because of this circumstance that we can now understand how they worked and why they had cut their stones in particular proportions according to the different requirements.

The problems were three-dimensional and to study them it is not enough to transpose them on to the flat surface of a drawing board. Each stage of the process needs to be assessed by reference to a model, when the true nature of the movements and geometrical forms involved will become obvious.

The student who wishes to master the problems will need to make his own models, and it may be helpful to read the descriptions which follow of my own attempts to bring the pyramid builders' work down to my own scale. The question of scale is an important one, and I came to discover that different parts of the operation needed to be reproduced to different scales, eventually ranging from full size, for the levers, down to 1/900th for the whole pyramid.

Pyramid models, hollow and solid

I decided that if I was to spend months, or even years, studying pyramids, then I needed to have a model of the shape as a daily reference and that this needed to be a portable model which could stand on the desk or bookshelves. So, I asked experienced joiners from my own building firm to make a hollow plywood pyramid – base 12 inches, pitch 52° – and was surprised that they found the task difficult. Carpenters could have constructed the same shape on a large scale by using rafters, without even the need to make a drawing (using the steel square as described in chapter 4), but joiners are not trained to deal with a skin-type construction. Any student of engineering or technical drawing will recognise the problem as one of intersection between inclined planes, and the simple process is to draw elevation and plan, develop (not calculate) the true angle between the sloping sides at the hip, cut the bevels accordingly, and the four sides can be glued neatly together without the need for any internal framework. However, holding the four sides together while the glue sets is by no means as easy as it sounds, and no-one should criticise who has not tried for himself.

I did get my pyramid in the end, but I realised that it would be helpful to have another one, divided into layers so that the structure could be viewed at different constructional stages. The Egyptians themselves had seen their pyramids grow layer by layer, and I needed to visualise the image that they would have seen after the first few years of work. Mr Hopkins, the joiner, soon made a solid pyramid, by hand, with a base of about 10 inches and consisting of 13 layers of 12mm. ply held together on a central rod (see figs 100 and 101). Although the model is now three years old and has been much handled, the edges of each layer are as straight and sharp as a knife edge. The outer surfaces were neatly and accurately planed by hand, without any glasspaper finishing to blur the edges or hide the edge grain of plywood. The model looks so simple but really requires great skill to make.

The scale is approximately 1/900th of full size. The Great Pyramid base is about nine thousand inches long, so that a nine inch model would be one-thousandth of full size. Do not be fooled into reading some mysterious significance into the length of nine thousand inches, because the builders did their work long before inches were invented.

Figs 100 and 101 *A model pyramid cut by hand from pieces of plywood and held in position by a centre rod.*

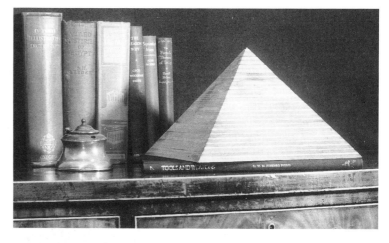

Levers (see figs 25–8, pp. 24–5)

The only possible way to test my lifting theory was to make a set of full-size levers and to test these out on a load weighing two-and-a-half tons. The factors which decided the general size and shape of the levers have been discussed in chapter 3 and on this basis I made some simple stress calculations which established that hardwood two-and-a-half inches square, strengthened with metal one-eighth of an inch thick on either side should be adequate to meet the likely loads involved. Subsequently I had a series of levers made, each developed from its predecessor, and these were numbered for reference purposes.

Lever no. 1 was tried without metal strengthening and, predictably, broke at the knuckle. Lever no. 2 (see fig. 102), was joined at the knuckle with multiple tenons and fitted with a

Fig. 102 *Lever no. 2 showing the tenoned knuckle joint and the wrought iron strengthening.*

Fig. 103 *Lever no. 2 – iron-shod – made to test the geometry of the lifting movement. Shown before the lift has begun.*

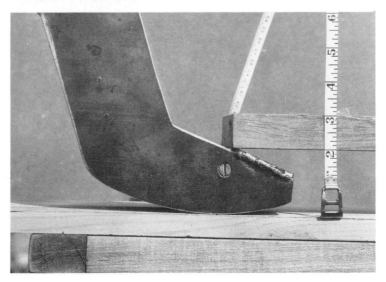

Fig. 104 *Lever no. 2 at the end of the lift. A gain of 4in shown.*

Figs 105 and 106 *Lever no. 5 – which can also be seen in action in figs 25–8, lifting the trial weight of two-and-a-half tons.*

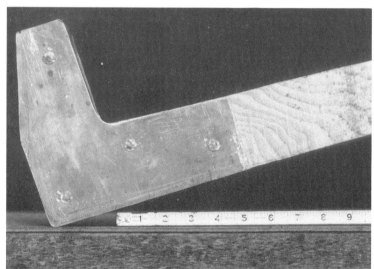

wrought iron shoe. This construction gave more than adequate strength so that experiments could be made to study the movements of the toe and the load without there being any risk of breakage and, as a result, lever no. 3 was made, having a straight instep and a slightly steeper angle between the shaft and the toe. This lever was cut from a plank of English ash and strengthened with one-eighth of an inch of brass sheet, riveted through the body with rods hammered at each end. The performance in practice matched up to the design so that this prototype was copied to make levers 4 and 5 (see figs 105 and 106), the only difference being that the metal used was soft copper as the closest available match to that metal which would have been used by Egyptians of the Third Dynasty.

I appreciate that the Egyptians would not have designed their levers from the basis of a stress calculation but would have improved the design and general efficiency by years of practice with stones which needed to be larger and heavier with each succeeding pyramid. It must be safe to assume that men who could organise the building of a large pyramid could also evolve the best type of lever. They had one advantage in that they could choose pieces of timber which had a natural curve at one end so that some, at least, of the grain would run continuously from the shaft round into the toe. This factor would reduce the dependency on the metal strengthening, vital for my levers which came from straight-grained timber, producing cross grain along the toe.

If lever no. 4 can be taken as a basic design, then it is open to others to continue the experiments and improve this design in any way, within the condition that no more than four men must be able to lift two-and-a-half tons through a worthwhile vertical gain.

My design requires 1,443 press-downs to reach the top of the Great Pyramid.

The Pyramid Game (see fig. 75, p. 79)

This model is so simple that it needs no explanation. It can be made from any pieces of board which have one exact right angle; the exercise can be made more realistic if the pieces are of different thicknesses, because the courses of the pyramid are not themselves of the same thickness. The consequence of this is that the steps vary in width as well as height and each new course must be set according to the gradient. It is not at all easy to set the pieces down sufficiently accurately to ensure that the hip points finish up in a straight line.

Pyramid model, building blocks (see fig. 80, p. 90)

It might be instructive to build a complete pyramid using miniature blocks, but it would be a wasteful operation because such a large proportion of the 2,300,000 blocks would be merely filling and would not help towards solving the constructional problems. I made for myself about 300 wooden blocks, all of the same size and with the length twice the width, for convenience in bonding them together. The pyramid blocks are not of this simple proportion, but this difference does not affect the validity of the various experiments I made, which included putting the blocks together in various forms as an aid to the imagination, and building up part of a hip line using some blocks which had been cut with a mitre bevel. The blocks are quite small, the rise being six inches for five courses, but the Great Pyramid to this scale would reach half way up the roof of my house, with a base side of just over thirty feet and a weight, in wood, of about 150 tons. The cost today, (1977), if the blocks were of oak would be about 6p each, or £138,000 for the lot, without the labour of putting them together.

The model in the photograph is made up of about two hundred of my blocks and, if the experts have been right in their assessment of the building period for the Great Pyramid, then that model represents the equivalent of a morning's work for the Egyptians.

The Apex Model (see figs 81–3, pp. 91–2)

If the pyramid was trimmed after completion then the masons needed a definite order and method for cutting away the steps so that the exact geometrical shape would not be lost. This is not so easy as it sounds, and so it was essential that I should try out this operation in the solid form and deduce the problems and the solutions just as they had been presented to the Ancient Egyptians. Obviously, the critical problem was how to begin, and to assess this I needed a model of the top of the pyramid as it would look after the last stone was laid and before the trimming began; furthermore, this particular model needed to be fairly soft so that I could carve the material away as the masons had done.

The model is made of balsa wood blocks, the centre of each course being filled in with chipboard squares. The apex stone is the top part of my divisible pyramid model. There is only one way to construct this model, and that is to follow the sequence used by the pyramid builders themselves; after constructing a square base, form each course consecutively by laying the corner stones, laying the side blocks and filling in the centre. You will need a bevel (to set the gradient), a square, a straight edge, and quite a lot of patience, but you will come to understand, and to master, the difficulties of building a pyramid. The bevel is, of course, a substitute for the plumbing frame (see fig. 39, p. 37), which would be difficult to use on a small model. A study of the finished model will show where the hip line lies and how essential it is to expose the four hips down the whole length of the figure before cutting off the steps. It is only by working in the solid that the actual conditions can be simulated.

Sliding the stones

I have drawn a diagram of the rig which I set up to test this theory (see fig. 107). I have not shown the details of its construction because these are something which the interested student can best work out for himself according to the materials which are to hand.

The amount of thrust required to move one stone over another will depend more upon the thickness of the upper stone than the area of the bed. I chose a stone with a bed equal to one-third of a square foot and then superimposed weights to give the equivalent of three feet thickness of stone. If both stones were thoroughly wetted to reduce suction and a grout made up of one part lime and one part soft sand were run in, then the load moved under an average thrust of 47lb. This suggests that a stone three feet thick and of sufficient size to weigh four tons would need the thrust of about sixteen men to achieve a short, sharp slide into its final resting place. There could be, say, four men pushing on a beam and three pulling on each of four ropes.

If you should do the experiment for yourself you will find that the essential element in getting the best lubricating effect from the grout is the use of a great deal of water. We know that water would have been hard to come by in large quantities, half way up a pyramid, and the provision of this essential commodity for all the building work is a subject which deserves further study.

Research and references

During these researches I have tried to use only those sources and those elements of knowledge which are available to any keen amateur, because I wanted to emphasise the point that there will always be an important place for the amateur in the the enjoyment and enlargement of the fine arts. The modern tendency towards deeper scholarship and closer specialisation has, if anything, increased the opportunities for the layman to employ his naive but wider observation in disclosing aspects of a subject which may have escaped the narrow focus of the expert. The professionals who spend a lifetime in the researching of our

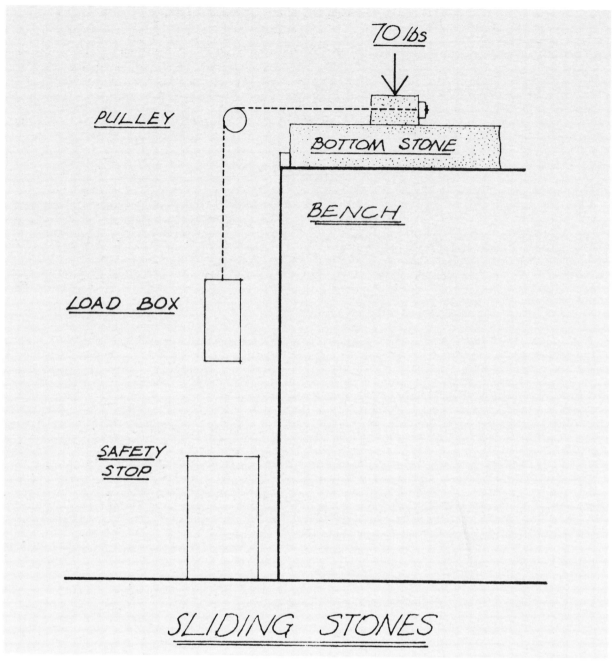

70 lbs

PULLEY

BOTTOM STONE

BENCH

LOAD BOX

SAFETY STOP

SLIDING STONES

Fig. 107 *Sliding stones.*

history do not do this only for themselves; they need the interest and participation of the educated majority for their work to become worthwhile.

Works of reference may readily be studied in most of the recognised libraries and museums and many of the important books may be read at home with the help of the existing library services; there is much assistance available for the serious student, but if the research is to follow an original path then it becomes essential to maintain a detached mind while reading the recognised authorities on any subject.

I was fortunate to have had the opportunity to make two visits to Egypt, but these would have been of little value without the benefit of the researches through books and photographs which are available to anyone. The first of these visits came about by chance in 1973, and was prompted by the fact that the whole cost would be less than £100, thanks to Egypt's wish to encourage tourism; the second was arranged in 1977 purposely to take photographs and make detailed observations, but again the nucleus was the standard package holiday of six-and-a-half days, with, in my case, two of these spent in bed while the pharaohs took their usual revenge, as they had done on my previous visit. The remainder was spent on special excursions which could have been arranged by any other tourist. The information which I needed in Egypt was so readily available because the tourist industry there has been organised since before the days of Herodotus specially to accommodate, guide and inform the curious of all nationalities.

Ramps and Levers

Additional material by the editor, Julian Keable

Ramps

Synopsis

If ramps were used in pyramid construction, then they must have been at a low enough gradient to permit their use: at 1 in 10 they might have been usable, but would stretch well beyond the main quarry area at Giza when serving the two largest pyramids there. They would also be three times more voluminous than the pyramids they were to serve. If placed so that they fed directly from the top of the quarry to the pyramid, then their gradient would have exceeded 1 in 7, and their volume would still be twice that of the pyramid they were to serve.

To build such a ramp would require suitable materials, much time, and (at least on the outside faces) skill and care. Petrie calculated that mud bricks would crush under their own weight before reaching the top of Khufu's Great Pyramid. But the use of stone is unthinkable in manpower and volume terms. All other materials fail to satisfy the need for stability.

The attached 'spiral' ramp, an apparently attractive alternative, fails to reach the top, proves to conceal several intractable problems in detail and, more seriously, would make it impossible to check the setting out during building since it would cloak the whole pyramid.

For the Great Pyramid, stones must reach the working plane at a rate of one every two minutes, if a twenty year building period is to be achieved, and if all the year is available. If the task must be done using only the ninety day 'inundation period' – the annual Nile flooding – then two blocks each minute must be delivered. With a single ramp, this implies gangs constantly moving at over 3kmph, without allowing for the time needed for the ramp construction; delays by any gang on the ramp will delay all the gangs behind too. But if two or three ramps were used, the volume problem escalates still further. Once delivered, the blocks also have to be placed in position, the outer ones at least to very fine tolerances.

A building method which avoids these problems would seem not only desirable, but essential. The fact that ramp building material is missing from the Giza plateau suggests that one was indeed found.

Problems

The problem of 'raising the stones' up the larger pyramids has exercised archaelogists from time to time, though to a lesser extent than the problems associated with the interior layout of chambers and passageways inside. I.E.S. Edwards, in his standard work *The Pyramids of Egypt*, devotes a chapter to the whole sequence of pyramid building; after quoting Herodotus on the subject he wisely adds: "...it must be admitted that Pyramid construction is a subject on which the last word has certainly not yet been written."[1]

At an early date, the idea that ramps were built was put forward, and has retained its hold over both the popular and the informed mind to this day. As recently as 1980, the *Atlas of Ancient Egypt* stated: "The only method *proved* to have been used by the Ancient Egyptians is based on ramps. These were inclined planes, built of mud brick and rubble, along which the blocks were dragged on sledges, (wheeled transport was not used in the pyramid age). As the pyramid grew in height, the length of the ramp and the width of its base were increased in order to maintain a constant gradient (about 1 to 10) and to prevent the ramp from collapsing. Several ramps approaching the pyramid from different sides were probably used."[2] (My italics: there is of course no proof.)

Ramp angles proposed

If this is accepted, the first key question that arises is: at what angle might a practical ramp be? On this, depends its volume.

The eminent archaeologist Borchardt encouraged his assistant Croon to study this question: Croon proposed a ramp of 20° in relation to the Meidum Pyramid, purporting to see the remains of such a ramp on the site. This represents an angle of 1 in 2.4; no one today seriously suggests that massive stone blocks could be dragged up so steep a slope.

Later, J-P. Lauer's drawing of the Great Pyramid ramp assumes a gradient of 1 in 3.[3] His drawing showed only a plan view, but a section can easily be constructed since we know the height up which the stones must be raised.

The recent *Atlas of Ancient Eygpt* speaks, as we have seen, more reasonably of a ramp at 1 in 10. The accompanying drawing however, (of course diagrammatically) shows, by inference from the side angle of the major pyramids, a slope of 1 in 2! The artist's problem was that a ramp of 1 in 10, if it is to reach the top of the Great Pyramid, must be 146m x 10 = 1,460m long (i.e. around one-and-a-half kilometres, or one mile). If a ramp of this, steep, but perhaps possible slope was built against the side of the Great Pyramid, where was it placed?

To the north lies a steep cliff. To the east and west, mastaba fields of early date makes it unlikely that a major ramp covered the area (see fig. 108). To the south seems more possible, not only

Fig. 108 *Map of Giza plateau, showing the three main pyramids. A ramp at a slope of 1:10 has been placed on the south face of the Great Pyramid – it overpasses the quarry from which the stone is to come.*

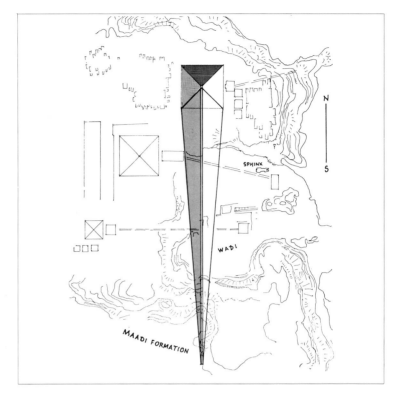

Fig. 109 *All three pyramids, with ramps which might be fed from the quarry. Slopes vary from 1:5.3 to 1:6.8.*

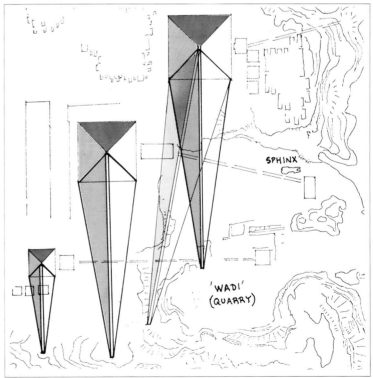

because the ground was clear, but also because the core block quarries lay in this direction. Measured from the top of the pyramid the distance to the south face of Menkaure's pyramid is some 800m; thereafter, the ground level, already falling, becomes more rapidly lower. Thus a ramp at 1 in 10 would stretch well out into the desert, or require to be doubled back on itself e.g. to the base of the pyramid. Put another way, a feasible ramp, in ground plan terms, leading directly from the quarry area south of Menkaure's pyramid, might be some 1000m long and thus rise at an angle of 146:1000, i.e. 1 in 7, provided it was laid out at a canted angle so as to arrive at the south-west head of the quarry (see fig. 109). M. Lehner et al. propose ramps stated to be 14° 37' 30"; this angle is in fact a gradient of 1 in 4.4. The report goes on to mention another proposal by Dr Haeny which assumes a ramp at the more gentle slope of 10° 41' 02"; a gradient of 1 in 5.3.

The ramp volume

A ramp at a slope of 1 in 7 and having a side gradient of 52° and a width of 10m on its top surface, would require some 5,596,107 m² of material to construct (base area x height x one third). To gain some idea of what an immense volume this is, it may help to set out some other figures.

The volume of the Great Pyramid when finished must have been some 2,600,000m³. Thus the proposed, rather steep, ramp at 1 in 7 would be some 2.15 times as voluminous.

The ramp material, if 'lost' by spreading over the ground to the height of a man (say 2m) would occupy 280 hectares after consolidation. (700 acres). If spread at 10m thickness (c. 33') it would still occupy 56 hectares (140 acres). At 10m thick, the area covered is some eleven times that of the Great Pyramid itself. Where is this material? It must be remembered that there are two other major pyramids on the plateau, which together would need as much material again for their ramps. Conceivably, some of this material might be re-used from an earlier to a later ramp, for inner 'rubble filling', but hardly for the outer and top surfaces.

Archaeology is largely based on finding things that people have thrown away – as time goes on, this is accepted more and more. (Petrie made potsherds respectable, where before him only mummies and gold were sought). It is unthinkable that 5,600,000m³ could disappear.

One obvious place to put the material would be back into the quarry out of which the stone was taken. Today, this quarry area is known as the 'Wadi'. It lies to the south of the pyramid plateau, and runs from east to west, rising from the east, (the Nile end), up to the west, not far from Menkaure's pyramid. The area of the Wadi, from its western end down to the level of the Sphinx (i.e. approximately the point to which the annual inundation would have come) is some 110,000 m² (11.0 hectares); the height from its lowest point at the Nile end to the plateau level at the Menkaure end is at most 40m; thus a maximum value of 4,400,000m³ can be set. It is unlikely that the Wadi was ever excavated below inundation level, so its volume can usefully be compared with that of the adjacent pyramids. Using the dimensions given by Edwards, but converting to metres, these are as follows:

$$\text{Khufu} \quad \frac{230.58^2 \times 146.7}{3} \approx 2,500,000m^3$$

$$\text{Khafre} \quad \frac{215.63^2 \times 143.7}{3} \approx 2,200,000m^3$$

$$\text{Menkaure} \quad \frac{108.58^2 \times 66.5}{3} \approx 260,000m^3$$

$$\textbf{Total volume} \approx \textbf{5,000,000m}^3$$

The Wadi (quarry) volume is thus some 90% of the gross pyramid volume, a reasonable fit given that facing blocks, tomb linings, passages and so on were constructed of better quality stone from elsewhere; that there are voids given by passages and chambers; and that the bases were probably not excavated to the external ground level internally, thus reducing the total volume to be filled.

By the same token, we can now see just how big the 'disposal problem' of the supposed ramp material really is. The Wadi is still there, partly filled with sand, but still steep sided and visible. Had the small ramps proposed by Mark Lehner (for example) been tipped into the quarry they would have filled it completely – no Wadi would be seen today. This volume problem becomes even more serious if we consider a believable ramp gradient. If we use the more realistic gradient of 1 in 10 proposed in the *Atlas of Ancient Egypt*, then, if such a ramp for Khufu's pyramid could start level with the pyramid base, it would have a volume of over 8,000,000m³ (see fig. 108). This is more than three times the Khufu pyramid volume, and equal to almost twice the Wadi volume for this one pyramid alone. It is of course also true that such a ramp cannot be sited on the Giza plateau – or rather that it would stretch right into the nearby hills or 'maadi formation' (see figs. 108 and 109).

Materials for construction

Martin Isler's scholarly, and at the same time practical approach to pyramid construction opens by considering possible ramp building materials.[5] He surveys various candidates, and concludes that:

△ wood is unthinkable because of the quantity required of this scarce material

△ burnt bricks were unknown in the Third and Fourth Dynasties (the period at which the great pyramids were built)

△ sand could only be used at its own (shallow) angle of repose, and so would smother the pyramid completely during construction

△ mud brick is clearly a candidate, but is limited by its own strength to 380 feet (as Petrie calculated: it would crush under its own self-weight beyond this) then the last 100 feet in height may itself prove a bigger problem than Petrie allowed, and

△ using stone would have taken an unacceptably long time to build.

He omits one other possibility sometimes put forward, namely stone chippings. A recent study by M. Jones and A. Milward did reveal where some of the stone chippings worked off the facing and core blocks went to – they are still, as one would expect, there on the site, right next to the Great Pyramid, and indeed in many places on the plateau where excavations have sunk through the upper layer of sand.[6] This discovery has prompted the suggestion that the stone waste itself may have been used to form the ramps.

Anyone who has seen a mine tip can imagine such a ramp – by definition it must be built by tipping the waste and nothing steeper that the angle of repose for the material used will do. This may prove to be some 20° (possibly Croon's ramp angle came from material that had fallen around the Meidum pyramid, and remained at its natural slope). If so, the volume required is much larger, of course, than the calculation at 52° – about 2.6 times as much in fact. Even if the Egyptian stonemasons were so wasteful that they produced as much waste as useful stone blocks, there would still be nowhere near enough for the required ramp by a factor of 8:1.

A further problem with this idea is of the inherent instability of such a structure: slag-heap slippages and scree slope stone chutes can give some idea of the difficulties to be encountered over a twenty year period.

The small amount of waste that has been found is quite consistent with the quantity of chippings to be expected from the dressing of the stones both before being raised into position, and from smoothing the facing stones on the pyramid face itself: moreover the chipping layers are in the right order for this, with the facing limestone on top of the core block chippings. It is not consistent with major ramp construction.

The Spiral Ramp

Some theorists, partly aware of the 'volume problem' (though not exposing it in any detail, it would seem) have proposed that the ramps were placed against the sides of the growing pyramid. This has the potential of reducing the volume of material dramatically and so it deserves careful examination.

A diagram of such 'spiral ramps' is shown in the *Atlas of Ancient Egypt*.[7] By inspection, it can be seen that the ramps shown are not in fact of constant gradient. By making a scale drawing it is immediately apparent why: The higher up the pyramid we go, the shorter becomes the length of side, and hence, at constant gradient, the less height we will gain (see fig. 110). Thus the first ramp, rising from a base length of 230m, actually only has 214m before it reaches the next corner, having risen some 21.4m. At this height the 'base Square' has shrunk to 214m, but the second ramp length will only be some 184m and the rise will thus only be 18.4m. At each turn, this effect is repeated until towards the top less than 1m is gained at each turn. The last blocks must once again be raised in some other way!

The real problem though concerns the construction of this ramp. At first, the side angle is unconstrained, for each of the first four turns (assuming only a single ramp and not two as shown in the *Atlas*). At the second series (i.e. the fifth ramp) this is no longer true. The width of the ramp ensures that the side angle must be greater than the pyramid side (52°), if the material is not to engulf the first ramp. At the third series, starting with the ninth ramp, this angle becomes steeper still, since less height has been gained. In fact, as the drawing shows, before the top is reached the ramp sides are required to be vertical; even using stone, this would have been difficult for such high walls and presupposes the need for 10m high scaffolds (themselves at 100m above ground level), in order to construct the ramp itself (see fig. 111).

A further problem with spiral ramps concerns the corners. Dragging a heavy stone requires a team of 75 men, and the need for at least 25m in length for the stone (on a sledge) plus the team. To pull such a weight round a corner would be extremely difficult, if not impossible. It would certainly slow the work down. The alternative, that of extending the ramp straight on, seems at first more attractive, but once again proves difficult at the upper levels. It would seem that a fairly sophisticated timber scaffold would be needed, so as to allow the lower ramp to pass underneath the upper corner.

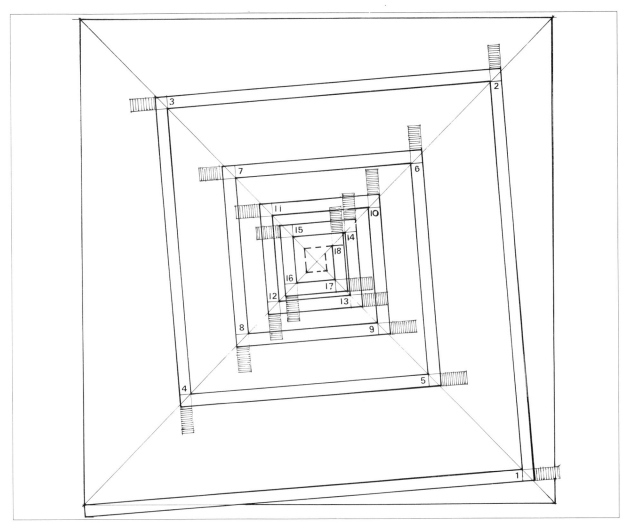

Fig. 110 *Plan of the Great Pyramid, showing an attached (spiral) series of ramps, at a slope of 1:10. At the end of each ramp, a scaffold is shown, to permit the hauliers to bring the stone to the corner itself. These scaffolds overlap by ramp 11. The ramps themselves exceed the space available for them before the top is reached.*

Last but not least we have the problem of how the setting out of the work could be achieved, when the entire pyramid was shrouded in ramp material. A ramp against one side only would leave three sides and all four arrises visible (provided no 'foot-hold embankments' are needed for placing the facing blocks) – not so the spiral ramp, under which nothing whatever can be seen. The ramp would permit the transport of core blocks and unfinished facing blocks. In order to finish off the pyramid, careful checking and alignment would be needed, especially of the arrises, so that the final dressing of the facing blocks would be 'true'. The dressing must start from the top, since there would be no foot-hold once the steep faces were smoothed off. More-over, that the four arrises must meet at a single point makes it certain that the work would be done from the top down. There-fore, before the final dressing could be done, the ramp would have to be completely removed. True, the volume of material would be very much less than with a straight ramp – only 10% or so of that of the pyramid volume.

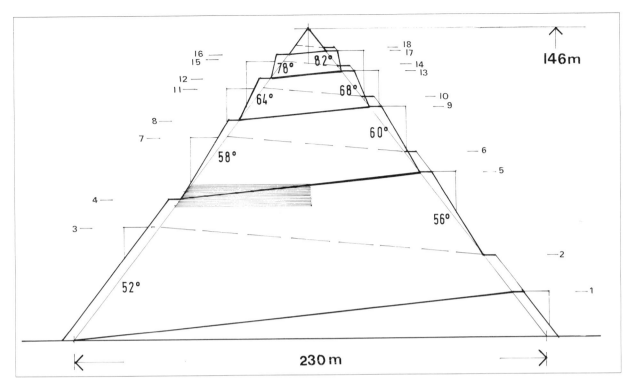

Fig. 111 *Side view of fig. 110. The ramps must have progressively steeper sides if they are not to mask the lower layers. Before the top, they are vertical, with 10m still to rise. This effect is independent of ramp angle.*

Block flow

Taking all these difficulties together it seems important to establish what width of ramp, whether straight or spiral, could accommodate the necessary number of teams.

No-one knows just how long the pyramids took to build. Khufu reigned 23 years and it is usually assumed that he must have virtually completed the Great Pyramid in that time. Recently, it has been shown that more than one pyramid was constructed at once. At the peak period, however, the 2,300,000 blocks, each weighing 2.5 tons on average, contained in his pyramid must have been raised in about 20 years, so we take this as the starting point. Clearly not less than 115,000 blocks a year must be raised.

A modern construction manager would certainly give great attention to this block-flow problem. In 20 years, assuming a 10-hour working day, and 360 working days a year(!), then 0.53 blocks per minute must be delivered. If it be assumed, as is usually said, that the main work force was only available for the three month inundation period, then only some 90 days must suffice. Each day, then, over 1,275 blocks must be delivered for placing, and now 2.1 blocks must arrive every minute.

We must bear in mind that each block must also be placed in position, right way up, snugly to its neighbour, and any tackle needed for the job cleared ready for the next stone.

How fast must teams be moving, if only one ramp is used?

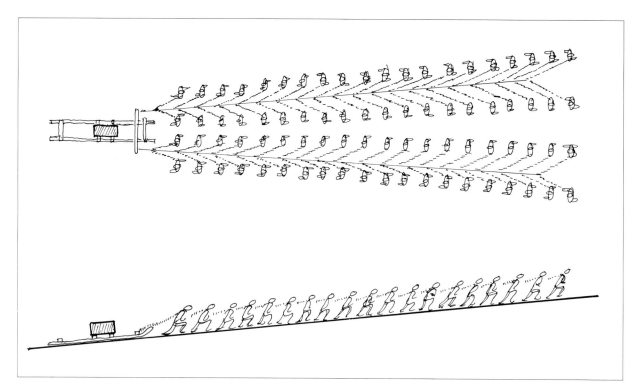

Fig. 112 *A block hauling team of 76 men. The team must move at 3kmph; if it stops, all the teams behind will be delayed too.*

If a block weighing 2.5 tons is placed on a 'sledge', some 5m long (see examples in the Cairo Museum), weighing say 0.25 tons, and assuming a man can pull (uphill!) 36kg, then some 76 men are needed for each team. Various arrangements are possible; 4 x 19 men might be convenient, and so, allowing 1m between men in line, over 25m is required in length, and perhaps 7m in width (see fig. 112).

To deliver blocks at the required rate thus needs the teams to move at over 3kmph. Of course, the ramp must be wide enough for the gangs to return to the quarries with their empty sledge, so at least 10m width will be needed.

The situation is not, however, as easy as this: time must be allowed for the construction of the ramp itself. This is usually referred to as being of mud-brick (and as we said earlier, steep side angles are needed to prevent the ramp volume growing even larger). Mud bricks have limited strength and to think of them as being used to build a ramp means that they must bear stresses relative to the weight of the entire ramp. Diagrams such as that in *The Atlas of Ancient Egypt* show a side slope equal to that of the pyramid side, i.e. 52°, which means that when the top courses are being placed, the ramp will exactly fill the whole south face of the pyramid. Any less steep angle presents the problem that it will 'spill over' onto the other faces by the time the top is reached. But let us agree that 52° is not so much greater than the angle of repose and that it is feasible. What is implied, however, must be faced. It is stated that the ramp will be lengthened as the greater height needed is required. To lengthen the ramp means to build out each face by the proportional amount needed.

At the outset, to add 1m in height to a 1 in 10 ramp which is 10m wide would mean building 10m² in area for the ramp sides, besides adding the more obvious 100m² in area to the ramp surface itself and would require 36m³ of material.

To add a second metre in height means adding a further 30m² in area for the ramp sides, plus a second 100m² of ramp surface, and would require a further 43m³ of material.

This slowly escalating effect produces the need, when building the last metre in height for the Great Pyramid, for an additional 2,650m² of 'ramp-side-area', requiring 186,484m³ of material. Only 14,600m³ of this material is for the ramp surface; the remaining 171,884m³ must be added to the ramp sides, placing the material securely, at heights up to 146m above ground level.

As to how the sides are to be built, is quite another question. In fact, the only feasible solution would seem to be that the full width finally required at the base should be built at once, so as to permit the steep sides to be undertaken sequentially, and not by the structurally unsound method of external accretion (see table 5).

Table 5

The Great Pyramid, showing stages of construction if a full width ramp at 1:10 was used. The final ramp volume is 3.3 times as great as the pyramid itself.

Height of Δ (m)	10	20	30	73	146
Volume of Δ (m³)	493,544	919,594	1,283,111	2,032,038	2,574,209
% of total volume	19	36	50	79	100
Length of R (m)	100	200	300	730	1460
Volume of R (m³)	73,326	283,305	607,439	3,063,868	8,525,547
R volume as% of Δ volume	15	30	47	150	331

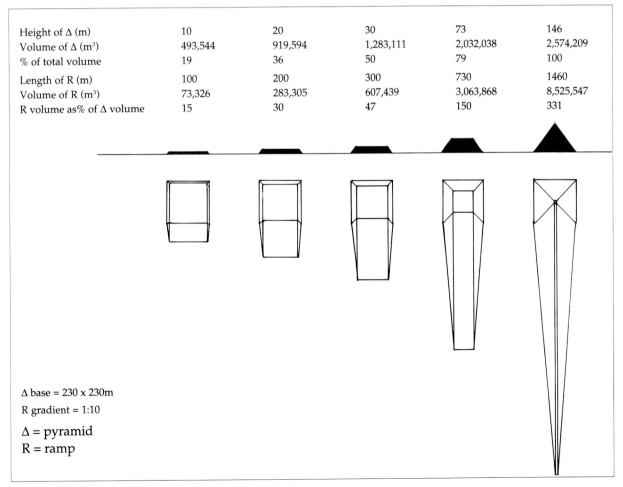

Δ base = 230 x 230m

R gradient = 1:10

Δ = pyramid

R = ramp

Using this method, as the pyramid grows in height the ramp width will slowly diminish, as the side angle bites into the landing area, in step with the diminishing pyramid working plane. The transport of the ramp building material itself up the ramp represents a larger task (in volume terms) than that of the pyramid itself, and although each mud-brick is not heavy, large numbers of people would be needed.

If we assume, as before, that each man can carry 36kg of mud-brick, a scarcely credible figure, even allowing for the 'rest' given by the weight free return journey, (bricklayers today carry about half of this in their hod), then the 16 million tons of mud brick required for the ramp represent 448 million man-hours, allowing one hour for the round trip (the mud bricks would have to be made near the Nile, where water and mud would be available). Each year, 25,000 men would be needed, assuming nothing but ramp construction has to be achieved; the bricks must be made too, of course.

We can now sum up the block-flow problem :

To haul up the stones, assuming 76 men per block and a 900 hour working year (90 days x 10 hours!) and moving constantly at more than 3kmph would suffice to raise the blocks to the working plane, assuming the ramp was in position – but with no time to build the ramp.

To build the ramp, 25,000 men are needed if the whole 90 day period is allocated, just to move the mud-bricks into position. The 800,000 tons a year must also be placed of course, requiring semi-skilled men at least at the outer edges. Care must be taken to avoid sloppy infill work too – a slip plane developing in the side of the ramp would require difficult and dangerous repair work.

To solve the conflict of double allocated time, we have to pre-suppose alternate working of block flow and ramp building. For example:

1 Build first 'course' of blocks

2 Build full ramp width

3 Deliver blocks for second 'course' up the ramp

4 Extend ramps … etc.

Note that the ramp width is always equal to the building platform, when using this method. Allowing for the 'full width ramp' described above might also solve the conflict of double allocated time, at least at the lower levels, if ramp building and block haulage could take place at the same time. If so, how many men would be needed?

Manpower

The round trip for hauling a stone to the working plane will be about 40 minutes per block, if the distance from quarry to pyramid is one kilometre, and travel is at 3kmph. Thus 15 trips per day could be made, allowing no time to rest. 1,275 blocks are to be delivered, so 85 teams are needed. Assuming a rotation of rest periods for the hauliers (but no stop for the block flow of course), some 100 teams x 76 men might be required – 7,600 men. This number is independent of ramp width.

We have seen that the larger task of building the ramps would have needed some 25,000 men to carry the bricks into position, and perhaps as many again to make them, and lay them.

For both tasks, a work force of 50,000 to 60,000 is indicated. Given that several of the assumptions made are well beyond what we would regard as reasonable limits, a more realistic number might be 100,000.

Such a number would represent a significant part of the total population, and it is for this reason that the idea was proposed that farmers, unable to farm during the annual flood, would have been drafted to the pyramid site, and the work done in 90 days only, each year.

Stone block placement

By assuming the ramp-building method, we necessarily assume also that the stones, once delivered to the upper working platform, can be placed at the same rate. Taking the median levels, at which some 10,000 blocks were being placed per 'course', it will be necessary for each of the block delivery gangs to be directed to a different part of the platform, so as to give time for the off loading and reasonably careful placing of the block itself. True, the inner core blocks need not be placed to the same incredible tolerances so often reported of the casing blocks; but if a 'stepped pyramid' is being built within the 'true pyramid', setting out is no mean feat.

What we see is that the stonemasons are receiving all their blocks in a 90 day period. They no doubt have a whole year at their disposal, but nowhere to stack them if the extra time is to be useful to them! How much more satisfactory if a method was used which assembled the stones at the foot of the pyramid, raising them up using a small, permanent, skilled gang, and placing them equally continuously throughout the year!

Late pyramids ('buttress pyramids')

During the Twelfth and Thirteenth Dynasties, many (smaller) pyramids were built, in which typically there were stone-buttressed ribs, and mud-brick or rubble infill. In so far as large stones were to be raised up the pyramid (including of course the outer casing blocks of fine limestone for dressing and polishing), all the same arguments apply as those which apply to Khufu's pyramid. The main difference would be that mud bricks for the pyramid itself could be taken up individually, and so greater flexibility would be possible in organising the work.

Robbing the stones

Almost all the casing stones were later robbed. This has had little effect on the solid stone structures, but has led to the complete erosion of the buttressed pyramids.

There are reports of the remains of 'construction ramps' associated with several pyramids. One of these supposed construction ramps seen annually by thousands exists inside the first pylon of the temple at Karnak.

Small, steep ramps may well have been a useful aid to casement stone robbing at times when such work could go on unhindered. They would assist in removing upper layers of cladding once the lower layers had been removed. (Higher up, the difficulty of removing casing stones has prevented Chephren's pyramid from losing all its casing.) They could be very steep indeed, since gravity would be doing all the work – which must nevertheless have been quite dangerous at times.

Conclusion

A building method that avoids the problems inherent in ramps, and requires far fewer men for the task of raising the stones to the working plane, would permit the work to be done on a year round basis. The farmers may still be drafted for work during the inundation period, but are then free to assist in the quarries, and in dragging the stones to the base of the pyramid.

By the same token, it would seem that the problems associated with ramp building are so great, and the quantities of material so enormous, that if this was (to quote Edwards) "the only method open to them" of building a pyramid it is scarcely credible that any would have been built.[8] If this be conceded, then it follows that some other method which avoids the need for ramps was found, since the pyramids are there. Strong further confirmation that some other way was found is given by the lack of ramp material at or near the Giza plateau.

Levers

Peter Hodges went to considerable trouble to test his theory, including the design and modification of full size levers, which he had made and then himself used. He can no longer tell us why he arrived at the 'hockey-stick' end, which gave him some trouble to make, and has inherent weakness at the knuckle, so requiring special strengthening. It may be that he instinctively felt that lifting from below the block was to be preferred to lifting at the edge; certainly when I discussed this with Mr Jones the stone-mason, he pointed out that continual edge-lifting would almost certainly lead to damaged arrises, and should be avoided if the block was to be seen. Almost all the stone raised up a pyramid is in fact not seen, so this reason would not have any great importance for the pyramid builders.

Peter invited archaeologists to look again at the accumulated finds, in case any objects whose purpose is unclear might provide evidence of the use of levers as a substitute for building ramps. There is indeed one interesting looking wooden tool to be seen in the Cairo museum, classified as an 'adze', which could possibly be used as a small lever; moreover, the 'nose' is worn in just the place to be expected if this was so. It is certainly much too small for lifting a major block, and the knuckle would not have much strength in it. (Also, see p. 22.)

As I went on thinking, it seemed to me that an essentially straight lever, if workable, is much to be preferred. The problem of strength at the knuckle is avoided; it is in every other way a simpler, and more natural solution; and the only picture of a lever which we do know is indeed straight (see fig. 113).

Fig. 113 *Twelfth Dynasty tomb at El-Bersheh, showing the transport of a colossal statue. A lever is carried by 3 men.*[1]

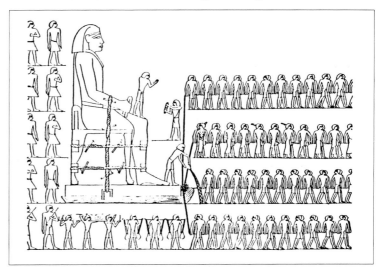

133

A drawing soon demonstrated that a straight lever is capable of delivering a 100mm 'lift' at each 'jack' (see fig. 114), so there seemed nothing to prevent a further experiment at full scale. My son Rowland, a trained cabinet maker, selected some oak spars, and we made a set of four levers which taper from 100mm at the fulcrum, to a 50mm wedge at the lifting point, and at the handles.

Fig. 114 *A straight lever, lifting point A to point B: 100mm. Note that fulcrum F is static; the lifting point slides along top surface of lever (A to B).*

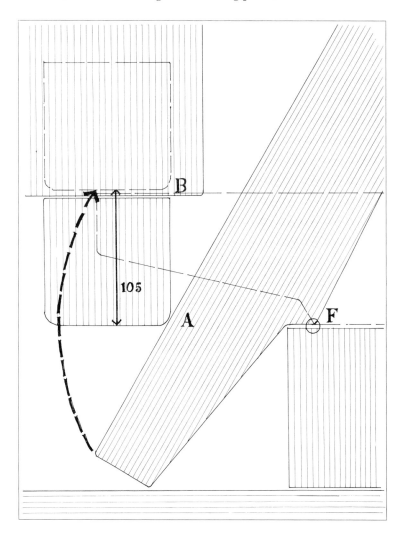

On Christmas Day 1986, having no two and a half ton stones to hand, we jacked up the Saab which weighed only 1.7 tons (see fig.115). This showed us several things:

∆ the force needed was easily produced.

∆ the moment of initial lift is accompanied by an **outward** thrust on the fulcrum block. This needs a light restraint.

∆ a 125mm lift was possible, jacking through 45°.

∆ it would have been pleasanter in Egypt – it was raining that morning!

Fig. 115 *The four straight levers lifting 1.7 tons, on Christmas morning 1986.*

Peter's crooked lever works in a different way. With his, the lifting point is static, whilst the knuckle slides during the jacking process. With ours the opposite happens; the fulcrum rolls over the block below it, so the lifting point is obliged to slide. With Peter's, the outward thrust noted in 2 above does not occur, which may be another reason for his design choice.

We discovered one more thing; as the fulcrum is raised after each successive 'jack' and placing of packing blocks for the stone to rest on, the possibility of achieving a 45° swing depends either on starting the lever at a higher point, or finishing lower – lower than the fulcrum in fact. Since the handle soon becomes too high to reach (at 45°), the latter becomes desirable. This lead to the idea of using a log as the actual fulcrum, rather than a flat block. By lashing a light spar between the two logs (on either side of the block to be lifted) the restraint required at 2 can be achieved.

Early in January 1987, we tried out this arrangement in the following way:

Where we live, there is a concrete sided slot, 1m wide, and 3.5m long, and 0.76m high, intended as a car maintenance pit. We had a pallet made, and obtained a load of dense concrete blocks; we found that by placing 14 blocks per layer, it would need 140 blocks to produce a weight of 2.5 tons. Having placed the pallet into the bay, we started to load the blocks. During loading, we saw that the pallet was not strong enough – it sagged between the end supports, and we stopped when only one ton was in position. We then attempted a lift, using the four levers, one man to each. Logs restrained by joining them with light spars were used as the fulcrum.

The lift worked easily, and we secured a 100mm 'jack', by placing a 100mm thick concrete block under each end of the pallet. However, whilst jacking, the load shifted position a little, and this movement was repeated during the second lift, to the point where this prevented inserting the next packing block. Why the load shifted was not completely clear:

Δ poor team work (leading to one end rising first, then shifting towards the other)?

Δ sloping ground?

Δ the fulcrum-log rolling, instead of staying in place? (We now think the fulcrum should be basically flat.)

In February we had obtained a stronger pallet, and could load the full two-and-a-half tons. This was done; but several small changes had noticeably large effects:

Δ in adjusting the fulcrum arrangement, the distance between fulcrum and weight was increased, leading to noticeably increased effort to lift.

Δ at the same time, the jack was thereby reduced to just under 100mm, making it impossible to insert a packing block.

A further vital point was that the pallet used softwood spars where the lever was applied, and these splintered under the load. This time the load shifted in the opposite direction, to the extent that there was too little space for the levers to operate at the closed end of the pit.

The forces involved with the 2.5 ton lift are approximately as follows:

$$\text{Lifting force} \times 2\text{m} = 1.25 \text{ tons} \times 0.1\text{m}$$

$$\text{Thus lifting force required} = \frac{1.25 \times 0.1}{2}$$

$$\mathbf{= 0.0625 \text{ tons}}$$

Since two levers are employed at each end, each has to be supplied with 0.03125 tons lift, i.e. 31kg: this force is needed during a sustained pull lasting perhaps 10 seconds. The jacker's body weight can hold the lever down (both levers if need be) while the packing block is inserted.

If the fulcrum is moved by only 25mm, then the lifting force required is increased to 40kg, using the same sized lever and weight as above.

The weather then stopped these experiments, and other matters prevented their early resumption. However, in September 1987 we demonstrated the three basic actions required to build a pyramid, using the same straight levers:

1 Sideways travel (see figs 116–9). By placing the 'block' (demonstrated by using a one ton load) on spars, which can be moved each time the load is taken off them, and by using a similar pair of spars on the ground adjacent, to act as the lever fulcrums, a 'paddling' action can produce sideways travel with ease. (Each lever is placed at 45° to the block – on plan – then pressed down, moved over through 90°, and lowered again). We moved our block 190 mm in one paddle, taking 20 seconds to do so. This gave a theoretical speed of 0.57m per minute, or 34m per hour. A block could thus be moved the full length of the pyramid base in under seven hours.

2 Vertical lift (see figs 120–23). We again placed our one ton load in the car repair pit, and jacked it up to the top. Eight x 100mm jacks gave an overall lift of 813mm. As the load was placed on a 100mm packing to start with, this cleared the 763mm sides of the pit.

During the first two jacks, the load shifted, about 37mm on each occasion. The support packings were adjusted. We then found that by starting the lever action at a much steeper angle (about 75°), and with the fulcrum closer to the load (90mm), greater control and a more vertical lift was obtained.

Fig. 116 *The levers placed ready for 'sideways travel'.*

Fig. 117 *The 'paddling' movement, down-and-across, in progress. The block is clear of its support.*

Fig. 118 *The levers raised again, to drop the block back on its support. Note that the lever handles are now beyond the block.*

Fig. 119 *The block has moved to the right: the white stick (aligned with end of pallet in fig. 116), is now 190mm away.*

Fig. 120 *The block is placed in the pit, ready to be raised up. The levers are in their starting position.*

Fig. 121 *The lift in progress.*

Fig. 122 *A 'jack' of over 100mm has been made, permitting a packing block of 100mm to be inserted.*

Fig. 123 *Nearing the top of the pit. Note the steep angle of the levers, and the packing needed for the jacking team, as well as the blocks.*

By the third jack we were taking 35 seconds per cycle (jack up, place packing, lower back onto packing); by the fifth jack this reduced to 25 seconds. In fact the jacking itself took only five seconds; placing the packings took most of the time, and it was clear that with practise, a much faster rhythm than ours would be possible.

Peter Hodges, in his progress chart calculations, assumed five minutes for each step. This is 34 seconds per jacking cycle, which now looks generous. Likewise he calculated it would take two days to move a block the full length of the Great Pyramid base; we think one day would suffice.

We worked with 90mm between the fulcrum edge and the load. Using the same basis of calculation as above, the force required to lift a 2.5 ton load at each of four lever ends would be 28kg – well below the possibility of any fit man, especially as the effort is only required in short bursts, and in rhythm.

3 Completing the step movement (see figs 124 and 125). We then placed spars between the packings and the pit side, and 'paddled' the block sideways, as we had practised on the ground. We were a little nervous of our one ton load, now supported at half our height above the ground, so we 'paddled' only 150mm or so each time. The packings under the load had to be moved so as to allow the lever tips to swivel round; otherwise no special problem was met.

Fig. 124 *A spar has been added, to permit sideways travel. The 'paddle' is in progress.*

Fig. 125 *The block is now displaced by half its own width.*

Figs 126–9 *show the operation on a pyramid.*

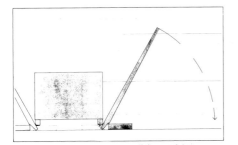

Fig. 126 *The levers in positions for the first 'jack': 2 each side, 4 in all. The stone block has been delivered on timber packings.*

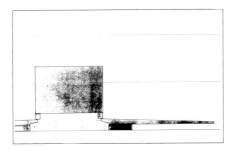

Fig. 127 *The first 'jack' is complete. An extra packing has been inserted below the stone at each end.*

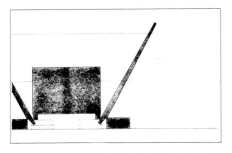

Fig. 128 *An extra packing has been added below the levers and the second 'jack' can be done.*

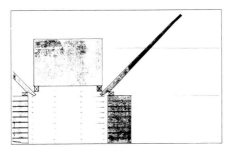

Fig. 129 *Eight extra packings and eight 'jacks' completed. The block is ready to be moved sideways, onto the next pyramid step.*

What other problems remain? Clearly, the facing blocks of a pyramid represent a special case; many theorists have concentrated their attention on this.

Petrie recorded the extent to which the course thicknesses vary; whilst there is a general diminution with greater elevation, thicker bands appear from time to time (see fig. 71). Thus a thick stone has sometimes to be lifted up over a thin bed.

To accomplish the lift using levers as described requires that additional blocking be used on shallow steps to permit the deep-coursed facings to be raised. Possibly small stone blocks, or simply a larger number of packings, would be used. The principle is unaffected. This same problem, and solution, would of course apply to the other special case of the capstone.

To sum up: straight levers could well have been used for the bulk of the lifting work. They may have had slots at the fulcrum (as is shown in fig. 113, the 'colossal statue' picture), to give a secure purchase; they may have had a hollow, to permit a ball-and-socket action when moving stones sideways. All that was needed was sound, strong, straight timbers, about two metres long in sets of four; 100 sets would be sufficient for the main work at the Great Pyramid, together with a few sets of larger levers to work the large stones over the chambers. A single shipment from abroad would have been sufficient.

Working a lever is a pleasure; carrying a 36kg load by main force is by comparison a punishment. It is quite possible to regard pyramid building as the top technology of the time, with the lever as the simple, but essential tool permitting the building process. Instead of needing 50,000–100,000 men simply to lift the stones, a force of 1,000 is needed – full time, specialist, skilled men of course, working on three of the pyramid faces at once.

Table 6 Imperial sizes and their metric equivalent

LENGTH

feet/inches (ft/ins)	metres (m)	example
1ft	0.305	
3ft 4ins	1	
756ft	230.58	length of Great Pyramid base
481ft	146	original height of Great Pyramid
4ins	0.102	
20.62ins	0.524	Royal Cubit, Fourth Dynasty
5280ft	1609	one mile

AREA

acres	hectares	example
1	0.4047	
2.471	1	
13.12	5.31	area of Great Pyramid

VOLUME

cubic feet (ft³)	cubic metres (m³)	example
1	0.0283	
35.31	1	
90,985,320	2,574,209	volume of Great Pyramid

MASS

pounds (lbs)	kilogrammes (kg)	tons	tonnes	example
1	0.4536	4.5×10^{-4}		
2.205	1	9.8×10^{-4}	0.001	
2,240	1,016	1	1.016	
2,205	1,000	0.984	1	
15,730,000,000		6,500,000		mass of Great Pyramid

References and Index

References

*Note by Margaret Hodges: where additional references have been put in by me, the author's note is applicable.

I am indebted to Diana Magee, research student in Egyptology, for assistance with reference material; and to the Griffith Institute, Oxford, for allowing me generous access to the Institute Library.

Author's note: some of the matters referred to may be seen in many publications, from which I have selected those most readily to hand.*

Short titles are given after full initial entries in each chapter.

Abbreviations

JARCE = Journal of American Research Centre in Egypt
JSSEA = Journal of the Society for the Study of Egyptian Antiquities

Chapter 1

1 Fakhry, A. *The Pyramids.* Chicago and London: University of Chicago Press, 1969.

2 Edwards, I. E. S. *The Pyramids of Egypt.* Harmondsworth: Penguin Books Ltd, 1972 edn, p. 265.

3 Edwards, *The Pyramids of Egypt.* p. 269.

4 Fakhry, *The Pyramids.* p. 251 (and referring J-P. Lauer).

5 Goneim, M. Z. *The Buried Pyramid.* London: Longmans, Green & Co. Ltd, 1956, pp. 65, 68.

Chapter 2

1 Edwards, I. E. S. *The Pyramids of Egypt.* Harmondsworth: Penguin Books Ltd, 1972 edn, p. 270.

2 Fakhry, A. *The Pyramids.* Chicago: University of Chicago Press, 1969, p. 13.

3 Fakhry, *The Pyramids.* p. 14, drawing 6 (after Croon).
   Lauer, J-P. *Observations sur les Pyramides.* Cairo: L'Institut Français, 1960, fig. 12.

4 Fakhry, *The Pyramids.* pp. 12–13, drawings 4–5.

5 Grinsell, L. and Dyer, J. *Discovering Regional Archaeology* Wessex. Tring: Shire Publications, 1971, pp. 65–6 (and referring R. Atkinson).

6 Edwards, *The Pyramids of Egypt.* pp. 271–2.
   Aldred, C. *Egypt to the end of the Old Kingdom.* London: Thames and Hudson, 1965, pp. 85–6.
   Macauley, D. *Pyramid.* London: Sir William Collins Sons & Co. Ltd, 1976, pp. 50 et seq.

7 Macauley, *Pyramid.* p. 39 et al.

8 Edwards, *The Pyramids of Egypt.* p. 271 (and also note Fakhry, *The Pyramids.* p. 13).

9 Goneim, M. Z. *The Buried Pyramid*. London: Longmans, Green & Co. Ltd, 1956, pp. 69–70.

10 Goneim, *The Buried Pyramid*. p. 71 and photo 25.

Fakhry, *The Pyramids*. p. 44.

11 Rowe, A. 'Excavations of the Eckley B. Coxe Jr, Expedition at Meydum, Egypt, 1929–30', *Museum Journal, University of Pennsylvania*. Philadelphia: 1931, plate IV (after Borchardt) – 'in Enstehung der P. – 1928'.

12 Goyon, G. *le Secret des Batisseurs des Grandes Pyramides*. Paris: Pygmalion, 1977, p. 72, fig. 19.

13 Lucas, A. *Ancient Egyptian Materials and Industries*. London: Edward Arnold (Publishers) Ltd, 1948, p. 160.

14 Grinsell, L. *Egyptian Pyramids*. Gloucester: John Bellows, Ltd, 1947, p. 66, fig. 7 (after W. Luker).

Edwards, *The Pyramids of Egypt*. p. 271.

15 Petrie, Sir W. M. Flinders. *Tools and Weapons*. Warminster: Aris and Phillips Ltd, 1974, plate XLIX no. 37 and p. 41, section 115.

16 Petrie, Sir W. M. Flinders. *Egyptian Architecture*. London: British School of Archaeology in Egypt and Bernard Quaritch Ltd, 1938, plate X fig. 62 and p. 40.

17 Petrie, *Egyptian Architecture*. plate X fig. 61 and p. 39.

18 Lauer, *Observations sur les Pyramides*. p. 54 (quoting Croon).

19 Lucas, *Ancient Egyptian Materials*. pp. 489, 491–4.

Chapter 3

1 Herodotus, *The Histories*. translated by Aubrey de Selincourt. Harmondsworth: Penguin Books Ltd, 1974, p. 179.

2 Rawlinson, G. *History of Herodotus*. edited by E.H. Blakeney. London: Everyman's Library, 1912, book II, 125.

3 Cottrell, L. *The Mountains of Pharaoh*. London: Pan Books Ltd, 1963, p. 251 (and quoting R. Engelbach).

4 Edwards, I. E. S. *The Pyramids of Egypt*. Harmondsworth: Penguin Books Ltd, 1972 edn, p.262 (and referring W.B. Emery).

Petrie, Sir W. M. Flinders. *Egyptian Architecture*. London: British School of Archaeology in Egypt and Bernard Quaritch Ltd, 1938, p. 31.

Lucas, A. *Ancient Egyptian Materials and Industries*. London: Edward Arnold (Publishers) Ltd, 1948, pp. 246 et seq.

Davies, W. V. 'Tools and Weapons I, Axes', *Catalogue of Egyptian Antiquities in the British Museum*. p. 117, chisel no. 37277.

5 Petrie, *Egyptian Architecture*. plate X fig. 59, and p. 38.

6 Petrie, *Egyptian Architecture*. pp. 37–8.

Edwards, *Pyramids of Egypt*. p. 275.

7   Edwards, *Pyramids of Egypt*. p. 45.

    Goneim, M. Z. *The Buried Pyramid*. London: Longmans, Green &
    Co. Ltd, 1956, pp. 9–10.

8   Petrie, *Egyptian Architecture*. p. 38

    Lucas, *Ancient Egyptian Materials*. pp. 500 et seq.

9   Petrie, *Egyptian Architecture*. plate X fig. 60 and p. 38.

10 Edwards, *Pyramids of Egypt*. p. 266 (and referring Somers Clarke
    and R. Engelbach).

11 Clarke, S. and Engelbach, R. *Ancient Egyptian Masonry*. London:
    Oxford University Press, 1930, p. 44.

Chapter 4

1   Edwards, I. E. S. *The Pyramids of Egypt*. Harmondsworth: Penguin
    Books Ltd, 1972 edn, pp. 119, 280.

2   The British Museum, London: Room no. 63, exhibit no. 37277.

3   Lucas, A. *Ancient Egyptian Materials and Industries*. London:
    Edward Arnold (Publishers) Ltd, 1948, pp. 252–3, 525.

4   Petrie, Sir W. M. Flinders. *Tools and Weapons*. Warminster: Aris and
    Phillips, Ltd, 1974, p. 42, section 116.

5   Newberry, Percy E. *The Life of Rekhmara*. Westminster: Archibald
    Constable & Co. Ltd, 1900, plate XX.

6   Baines, J. and Malek, J. *Atlas of Ancient Egypt*. Oxford: Phaidon
    Press Ltd, 1980, pp. 14–16.

Chapter 5

1   Baines, J. and Malek, J. *Atlas of Ancient Egypt*. Oxford: Phaidon
    Press Ltd, 1980.

2   Edwards, I. E. S. *The Pyramids of Egypt*. Harmondsworth: Penguin
    Books Ltd, 1972 edn, pp. 20–22.

3   Edwards, *Pyramids of Egypt*. pp. 55–7.

4   Fakhry, A. *The Pyramids*. Chicago: University of Chicago Press,
    1969, p. 19.

5   Edwards, *Pyramids of Egypt*. p. 261.

6   Mendelssohn, K. *The Riddle of the Pyramids*. London: Thames and
    Hudson, 1974, p. 73.

7   Clarke, S. and Engelbach, R. *Ancient Egyptian Masonry*. London:
    Oxford University Press, 1930, p. 62.

8   Herodotus, *The Histories*. Translated by Aubrey de Selincourt.
    Harmondsworth: Penguin Books Ltd, 1974, p. 131.

9   Clarke and Engelbach, *Ancient Egyptian Masonry*. p. 63 (and
    referring Petrie).

Chapter 6

1   Fakhry, A. *The Pyramids*. Chicago: University of Chicago Press, 1969, p. 6.

Edwards, I. E. S. *The Pyramids of Egypt*. Harmondsworth: Penguin Books Ltd, 1972 edn, p. 97 (quoting Sir J. G. Wilkinson and J. S. Perring).

Mendelssohn, K. *The Riddle of the Pyramids*. London: Thames and Hudson, 1974, ch. V.

2   Edwards, *The Pyramids of Egypt*. Harmondsworth: Penguin Books Ltd, 1972 edn, p. 53.

3   Mendelssohn, *Riddle of the Pyramids*. p. 115 (and see fig. 8[F], pp. 36–7, after Borchardt).

Edwards, *Pyramids of Egypt*. pp. 268, 269 (referring Borchardt).

4   Edwards, *Pyramids of Egypt*. p. 92, and fig. 17.

Mendelssohn, *Riddle of the Pyramids*. pp. 45, 81, 85 et seq.

Lauer, J-P. *Le Probleme des Pyramides d'Egypte*. Paris: Payot, 1948, fig. 24, p. 89, "after Borchardt".

Fakhry, *The Pyramids*. p. 69.

5   Rowe, A. 'Excavations of the Eckley B. Coxe Jr, Expedition at Meydum, Egypt, 1929–30', *Museum Journal, University of Pennsylvania*. Philadelphia: 1931, plate X.

6   Borchardt, *Einiges zur Dritten Bauperiode der Grossen Pyramide bei Gise*. Berlin: Julius Springer, 1932, plate 1.

7   Grinsell, L. *Egyptian Pyramids*. Gloucester: John Bellows, Ltd, 1947, fig. 9, p. 104.

Mendelssohn, K. *Riddle of the Pyramids*. fig. 8[F], pp. 36–7.

8   Edwards, *Pyramids of Egypt*. pp. 122, 268.

9   Grinsell, *Egyptian Pyramids*, p. 103

Chapter 7

1   Goneim, M. Z. *The Buried Pyramid*. London: Longmans, Green & Co. Ltd, 1956.

Fakhry, A. *The Pyramids*. Chicago: University of Chicago Press, 1969, pp. 42–4.

2   Fakhry, *The Pyramids*. p. 13.

3   Edwards, I. E. S. *The Pyramids of Egypt*. Harmondsworth: Penguin Books Ltd, 1972 edn, p. 275.

Clarke, S. and Engelbach, R. *Ancient Egyptian Masonry*. London: Oxford University Press, 1930, p. 86 and figs 99–100.

Chapter 8

1   Mendelssohn, K. *The Riddle of the Pyramids*. London: Thames and Hudson, 1974, pp. 116–17.

2 Fakhry, A. *The Pyramids*. Chicago: University of Chicago Press, 1969, p. 14.

Edwards, I. E. S. *The Pyramids of Egypt*. Harmondsworth: Penguin Books Ltd, 1972 edn, pp. 282–3.

Chapter 9

1 Clarke, S. and Engelbach, R. *Ancient Egyptian Masonry*. London: Oxford University Press, p. 105, fig. 112.

2 Clarke and Engelbach, *Ancient Egyptian Masonry*. p. 121.

3 Jones, M. and Milward, A. 'Survey of the Temple of Isis, Mistress of the Pyramid at Giza', *JSSEA*. Toronto: vol. 12, report on the 1980 Season, 1982.

4 Edwards, I. E. S. *The Pyramids of Egypt*. Harmondsworth: Penguin Books Ltd, 1972 edn, p. 276 (referring Jequier).

5 Macauley, D. *Pyramid*. London: Sir William Collins Sons & Co. Ltd, 1976, and see p. 59.

Chapter 10

1 Edwards, I. E. S. *The Pyramids of Egypt*. Harmondsworth: Penguin Books Ltd, 1972 edn, pp. 275–6 (quoting Petrie).

2 Fakhry, A. *The Pyramids*. Chicago: University of Chicago Press, 1969, p. 13.

Macauley, D. *Pyramid*. London: Sir William Collins Sons & Co. Ltd, 1976, pp. 49–51.

3 Petrie, Sir W. M. Flinders. *Egyptian Architecture*. London: British School of Archaeology in Egypt and Bernard Quaritch Ltd, 1938, p. 49.

4 Petrie, *Egyptian Architecture*. p. 37.

Grinsell, L. *Egyptian Pyramids*. Gloucester: John Bellows, Ltd, 1947, p. 114.

5 Borchardt, L. *Langen und Richtungen der vier Grundkantem der Grossen Pyramides bei Gise*. Julius Springer. Berlin: 1926, plate 3 (and see reference [1], ch. 9).

6 Lauer, J-P. *Observations sur les Pyramides*. Cairo: L'Institut Français, 1960, p. 49.

Lauer, J-P. *Histoire Monumentale des Pyramides d'Egypt, I*. Cairo: L'Institut Français, 1962, pp. 252–3.

7 Fakhry, *The Pyramids*. p. 12.

8 Edwards, *Pyramids of Egypt*. p. 266 and fig. 56.

Fakhry, *The Pyramids*. p. 13, drawing 5.

9 Fakhry, *The Pyramids*. pp. 125–6.

Mendelssohn, K. *The Riddle of the Pyramids*. London: Thames and Hudson, 1974, pp. 154–5

10 Mendelssohn, *Riddle of the Pyramids*. p. 123, (quoting H.Vyse and J. S. Perring).

11   Edwards, *Pyramids of Egypt.* pp. 170–1.

12   Lucas, A. *Ancient Egyptian Materials and Industries.* London: Edward Arnold (Publishers) Ltd, 1948, p. 73.

Ramps

1   Edwards, I.E.S. *The Pyramids of Egypt.* Harmondsworth: Penguin Books Ltd, 1947, p. 270.

2   Baines, J. and Malek, J. *Atlas of Ancient Egypt.* Oxford: Phaidon Press Ltd, 1980, p. 139.

3   Lauer, J-P. *Observations sur les Pyramides.* Cairo: L'Institut Français, 1960, fig. 12.

4   Lehner, M. L. 'The Giza Plateau mapping project: season 1984–85', *ARCE Newsletter.* Cairo: Fall 1985.

5   Isler, M. 'On pyramid building', *JARCE.* Cairo: vol. XXII, 1985.
      Isler, M. 'On pyramid building II', *JARCE.* Cairo: vol. XXIV, 1987.

6   Jones, M. and Milward, A. 'Survey of the Temple of Isis, Mistress of the Pyramid at Giza', *JSSEA.* Toronto: vol. 12, report on the 1980 season, 1982.

7   Baines and Malek, *Atlas of Ancient Egypt.* p. 139.

8   Edwards, *The Pyramids of Egypt.* p.270.

Levers

1   Edwards, I. E. S. *The Pyramids of Egypt.* Harmondsworth: Penguin Books Ltd, 1972 edn, p. 267.

Index

stone(s) average(standard) 6 *(and fig. 3)*, 18 *(fig. 22)*, 20, 29 *(and fig. 32)*, 31, 54, 62; casing 6, 87 *(and fig. 77)*, 105, 132; core *see* **core blocks/stones**; datum 43, 46; facing *see* **facing blocks/stones (casing)**; granite 30, 34, 91, 105; handling of 15, 20, 28, 70; heavy/large 6, 20, 29–31, 32, 81, 86–7; limestone 6, 34, 70, 74, 87, 89, 105, 125, 132; lowering of into final positions 100–104; movement of 11, 32, 104, 133 *(fig. 113)*; raising of 10, 16, 33, 120, *see also* **Giza**, raising stones at; for ramps 124, 125; at Saqqara 8; sliding the 93, 103, 104, 113, *114 (fig. 107)*; types of, for building 2, 3, 34; varying thicknesses of 73 *(and fig. 71)*, 74 *(fig. 72)*; weight of 6, 8, 28, 56, 65, 68, 74, 75 *(fig. 73)*, 81, 85–7; *see also* **Great Pyramid, the**

stonework anatomy of 53; progressive quality of 8–9

theodolite 48 *(and fig. 44)*, 49, 78
Third Pyramid of Giza 4, *see also* **Menkaure, Pyramid of**
timber *see* **wood**
tombs 5, 6, 23, 26; evolution of design of 40, 55; endowments to maintain 41 *(and note)*; principal, listed in sequence 54 *(table 3)*, 55; robbing of 41; at Saqqara 8, 38, 40; *see also* **mastaba tombs**
tools 1, 16, 22, 23, 26, 34, 35, 37, 38, 39, 133; *see also* **bevel, boning rods, chisel(s), cradles, gallows, jacks, levers, measuring rods, plumb board, plumb–bob, plumb line, plumbing frame, pulleys, set square, theodolite**
trimming (of stone) of the Great Pyramid 89; of hips 90, 91, 92; method of 87–95; model to show 91 *(and fig. 81)*, 92 *(figs 82–3)*, 112–13; timetable for 93; *see also* **stone arisings/chippings/residue**

Unfinished Pyramid, the 55, 67, *see also* **Sekhemkhet**

vertical gain 25 *(fig. 28)*, 83, 100, 111
vertical lift 20
vertical movement (of lever) 23
vertical plane 36, 77, 78

walls 55, 65, 71; battered 36, *see also* **face work (casing)** battered; buttress (retaining) 55 *(and figs 47–8)*; circular 76
water 103 *(note)*; evidence for use in levelling 36 *(note)*; for levelling 36, 42–3, 79; for reducing suction 103, 113; *see also* **irrigation; levelling, canal/channel for**
water transport 32
wedge 16
wedging 88
wheels 20, 32, 38; scaling ladder on 32
wood (timber) 3, 17, 18, 26, 28, 32, 40; blocks of, for model 112; cribbing (for ramps) 12 *(and fig. 12)*, 124; for levers 23, 24 *(figs 25–6)*, 26, 109, 111, 133, 134; for measuring rods, made of 45; *see also* **cedar wood, plywood**

Zoser 9 *(table 2)*; Pyramid of 4 *(and note)*, 8 *(note)*, 10, 40, 52 *(figs 45–6)*, 53, 54 *(and table 3)*, 55–6, 65 *(fig. 65)*, 100, 104